ST(P) MATHEMATICS 3A

Teacher's Notes and Answers

L. Bostock, B.Sc.
formerly Senior Mathematics Lecturer, Southgate Technical College

S. Chandler, B.Sc.
formerly of the Godolphin and Latymer School

A. Shepherd, B.Sc.
Head of Mathematics, Redland High School for Girls

E. Smith, M.Sc.
Head of Mathematics, Tredegar Comprehensive School

Stanley Thornes (Publishers) Ltd

First published 1985 by
Stanley Thornes (Publishers) Ltd,
Old Station Drive,
Leckhampton,
CHELTENHAM GL53 0DN

Reprinted 1986, 1987, 1988

British Library Cataloguing in Publication Data
ST(P) mathematics
    Book 3A Answers and teacher's notes
    1. Mathematics—1961–
    I. Bostock, L.
    510   QA39.2

    ISBN 0–85950–208–2

ST(P) MATHEMATICS will be completed as follows:

Published 1984	**ST(P) 1**
	ST(P) 1 Teacher's Notes and Answers
	ST(P) 2
Published 1985	**ST(P) 2** Teacher's Notes and Answers
	ST(P) 3A
	ST(P) 3B
	ST(P) 3A Teacher's Notes and Answers
	ST(P) 3B Teacher's Notes and Answers
Published 1986	**ST(P) 4A**
	ST(P) 4B
	ST(P) 4A Teacher's Notes and Answers
	ST(P) 4B Teacher's Notes and Answers
Published 1987	**ST(P) 5A** (with answers)
	ST(P) 5B (with answers)
Published 1988	**ST(P) 5C**
	ST(P) 5C Copy Masters
	ST(P) 5C Teacher's Notes and Answers
In preparation	**ST(P)** Resource Book

Typeset by Thanet Press, Margate, Kent
Printed and bound in Great Britain by Ebenezer Baylis and Son, Worcester

INTRODUCTION

This book is intended for use with pupils who are aiming at the highest level of GCSE Mathematics. We are aware that among these pupils are those who will eventually decide to aim for the middle level GCSE and these are the pupils we mean when we talk about the less able.

Those questions that are double underlined, e.g. **2**, should be used cautiously, if at all, with the less able. They are intended to give the brightest pupils food for thought but can easily damage the confidence of the others. Questions which are single underlined, e.g. **2**, are extra, but not harder, questions. They can be used as extra practice, for faster workers or later for revision.

Those pupils who by now are quite clearly not going to attempt the highest level maths papers should not be using this book. The parallel B series contains work designed specifically for them.

This book is large for two reasons. Firstly because it contains a lot of revision work and secondly because it covers a wide range of topics, not all of which will be in any one syllabus. The most able will benefit from a wide ranging coverage but with the less able it is probably wise to omit topics that are not necessary for examination purposes.

The text, though adequate, is brief and leaves ample scope for teachers to use their own methods and ideas, and to supplement the examples given. For a pupil who is revising a topic, the explanatory text is a useful reminder of the reasons for the methods followed.

The detailed notes that follow are only suggestions. Experienced teachers will have their own ideas on approach and order of content.

NOTES AND ANSWERS

CHAPTER 1   Making Sure of Arithmetic

This chapter is mainly revision, but the last section is new work. It can be worked through as consolidation of earlier work or parts of it can be used as and when necessary to act as reminders.

EXERCISE 1a   This exercise, together with Exercises 1b and 1c, can be used for discussion and provides a useful reminder of basic operations with fractions, before algebraic fractions—Chapter 24.

1. 21	**5.** 6	**9.** 42
2. 18	**6.** 20	**10.** 18
3. 40	**7.** 12	**11.** 24
4. 12	**8.** 60	**12.** 72

13. $1\frac{13}{24}$	**17.** $1\frac{17}{48}$	**21.** $2\frac{1}{5}$
14. $\frac{9}{10}$	**18.** $\frac{11}{12}$	**22.** $\frac{71}{126}$
15. $1\frac{29}{40}$	**19.** $\frac{8}{9}$	**23.** $1\frac{13}{24}$
16. 1	**20.** $1\frac{3}{4}$	**24.** $1\frac{23}{42}$

25. $\frac{13}{36}$	**27.** $\frac{7}{30}$	**29.** $\frac{1}{40}$
26. $\frac{1}{36}$	**28.** $\frac{1}{20}$	**30.** $\frac{5}{18}$

31. $3\frac{29}{40}$	**34.** $3\frac{11}{12}$	**37.** $4\frac{2}{15}$
32. $\frac{7}{18}$	**35.** $4\frac{7}{8}$	**38.** $\frac{1}{8}$
33. $-\frac{9}{40}$	**36.** $\frac{17}{20}$	**39.** $1\frac{1}{12}$

EXERCISE 1b

1. $\frac{5}{9}$	**4.** $\frac{1}{10}$	**7.** $\frac{4}{7}$
2. $1\frac{1}{3}$	**5.** $\frac{10}{21}$	**8.** 6
3. $1\frac{1}{2}$	**6.** $\frac{3}{10}$	**9.** $\frac{7}{22}$

10. 2	**12.** 3	**14.** $\frac{4}{3}$
11. 3	**13.** $\frac{3}{2}$	**15.** $\frac{8}{7}$

EXERCISE 1c

1. $\frac{1}{4}$	**4.** $\frac{1}{10}$	**7.** $\frac{1}{100}$
2. 2	**5.** 8	**8.** $\frac{9}{2}$
3. $\frac{5}{2}$	**6.** $\frac{11}{3}$	**9.** $\frac{4}{15}$

10. $1\frac{1}{3}$ **13.** $6\frac{1}{4}$ **16.** $\frac{12}{49}$

11. 2   **14.** $\frac{14}{81}$ **17.** $\frac{1}{18}$

12. $\frac{5}{8}$ **15.** $\frac{2}{3}$ **18.** $4\frac{1}{2}$

19. $\frac{13}{30}$ **22.** $2\frac{1}{18}$ **25.** $4\frac{23}{42}$

20. $\frac{69}{112}$ **23.** $5\frac{3}{10}$ **26.** $\frac{7}{20}$

21. $\frac{8}{25}$ **24.** $\frac{57}{110}$ **27.** $-\frac{1}{2}$

28. $3\frac{7}{12}$ **31.** $\frac{22}{63}$ **34.** $\frac{9}{50}$ **37.** $\frac{21}{68}$

29. $3\frac{3}{140}$ **32.** 14   **35.** $1\frac{2}{25}$ **38.** $1\frac{1}{4}$

30. $\frac{2}{5}$ **33.** 7   **36.** $\frac{1}{14}$ **39.** 2

EXERCISE 1d   This exercise, together with Exercises 1e, 1f and 1g, revises basic operations with decimals. If recurring decimals were not covered in Book 1, they can be discussed now.

1. $\frac{7}{20}$ **5.** $\frac{3}{100}$ **9.** $\frac{11}{100}$

2. $\frac{27}{125}$ **6.** $\frac{3}{250}$ **10.** $2\frac{1}{20}$

3. $\frac{51}{250}$ **7.** $\frac{1}{200}$ **11.** $1\frac{13}{125}$

4. $1\frac{9}{25}$ **8.** $1\frac{1}{100}$ **12.** $\frac{1}{10\,000}$

13. 0.15   **17.** 0.0625   **21.** 0.16

14. 0.125   **18.** 0.54   **22.** 0.3125

15. 0.6   **19.** 1.75   **23.** 2.375

16. 0.24   **20.** 0.156 25   **24.** 0.002

EXERCISE 1e   **1.** $0.\dot{3}$ **5.** $0.\dot{1}4285\dot{7}$ **9.** $0.41\dot{6}$

2. $0.\dot{2}$ **6.** $0.08\dot{3}$ **10.** $0.0\dot{7}1\,428\,\dot{5}$

3. $0.8\dot{3}$ **7.** $0.0\dot{9}$ **11.** $0.2\dot{3}$

4. $0.0\dot{6}$ **8.** $0.0\dot{5}$ **12.** $0.07692\dot{3}$

EXERCISE 1f   **1.** 5.01   **4.** 8.8   **7.** 4.832

2. 19.1   **5.** 1.82   **8.** 1.106

3. 6.17   **6.** 26.36   **9.** 0.002 02

10. 3.2   **13.** 1.21   **16.** 0.361

11. 3.3   **14.** 0.49   **17.** 1.83

12. 0.08   **15.** 23.02   **18.** 0.0068

19. 0.96   **22.** 0.01   **25.** 3.36

20. 0.042   **23.** 0.25   **26.** 3.355 11

21. 0.008   **24.** 0.360 72   **27.** 0.000 384

28. 7   **31.** 0.008   **34.** 1

29. 0.3   **32.** 0.015   **35.** 0.02

30. 2.7   **33.** 5.9   **36.** 0.001

37. 0.6	**40.** 129	**43.** 1	**46.** 0.2
38. 7.8	**41.** 11.882	**44.** 2	**47.** 0.4
39. 0.5	**42.** 3.094	**45.** 1.69	**48.** 8.95

EXERCISE 1g

1. <	**4.** <	**7.** >
2. >	**5.** >	**8.** >
3. <	**6.** >	**9.** >

10. $0.6, \frac{2}{3}, \frac{4}{5}$ **13.** $\frac{5}{7}, 0.75, \frac{7}{9}, 0.875$

11. $0.79, \frac{4}{5}, 0.85$ **14.** $\frac{3}{20}, 0.16, 0.2, \frac{6}{25}$

12. $\frac{1}{5}, \frac{2}{7}, 0.3$ **15.** $1\frac{1}{8}, 1\frac{1}{5}, 1.24, 1.3$

EXERCISE 1h   This exercise, together with Exercises 1i and 1j, revises the work on positive and negative indices from Book 2 but with harder examples. Fractional indices are covered in Book 4.

1. 25	**6.** 144	**11.** 325
2. 81	**7.** 1600	**12.** 8010
3. 32	**8.** 864	**13.** 720
4. 125	**9.** 2048	**14.** 1102
5. 64	**10.** 27 783	**15.** 1 100 000

16. 2^7	**19.** 5^4	**22.** 4^9
17. 3^7	**20.** 2^5	**23.** a^5
18. Not possible	**21.** 7^7	**24.** Not possible

25. 2^2	**28.** 4^3	**31.** 3^3
26. 7	**29.** Not possible	**32.** a^4
27. Not possible	**30.** 3^4	**33.** Not possible

EXERCISE 1i

1. $\frac{1}{2}$	**3.** $\frac{1}{5}$	**5.** $\frac{1}{8}$	**7.** $\frac{1}{a}$
2. $\frac{1}{10}$	**4.** $\frac{1}{7}$	**6.** $\frac{1}{4}$	**8.** $\frac{1}{x}$

9. 3	**11.** 4	**13.** 5	**15.** a
10. $1\frac{1}{2}$	**12.** $1\frac{1}{3}$	**14.** $1\frac{1}{4}$	**16.** $\frac{y}{x}$

17. $\frac{1}{8}$	**19.** $\frac{1}{1000}$	**21.** $\frac{1}{32}$	**23.** $\frac{1}{100}$
18. $\frac{1}{25}$	**20.** $\frac{1}{36}$	**22.** $\frac{1}{10000}$	**24.** $\frac{1}{64}$

25. 125	**27.** 32	**29.** 512	**31.** 8
26. 16	**28.** 81	**30.** 10 000	**32.** 36

33. $1\frac{7}{9}$	**35.** $5\frac{1}{16}$	**37.** $5\frac{1}{16}$	**39.** $123\frac{37}{81}$
34. $3\frac{3}{8}$	**36.** $12\frac{1}{4}$	**38.** $2\frac{7}{9}$	**40.** $2\frac{14}{25}$

EXERCISE 1j

1. 8	**6.** 1	**11.** $2\frac{10}{27}$	**16.** $\frac{64}{125}$
2. $6\frac{1}{4}$	**7.** 125	**12.** $3\frac{1}{2}$	**17.** $\frac{1}{12}$
3. $\frac{1}{16}$	**8.** $\frac{1}{9}$	**13.** 1	**18.** 729
4. 64	**9.** 16	**14.** $2\frac{314}{343}$	**19.** 64
5. 1	**10.** 1	**15.** $\frac{1}{4}$	**20.** 1

EXERCISE 1k   This revises standard form. For those with scientific calculators, Number 28 explains the notation used, but there is some variety in the display of scientific notation on different calculators.

1. 345	**4.** 0.0047	**7.** 902 000
2. 1200	**5.** 280	**8.** 0.000 637
3. 0.0501	**6.** 0.73	**9.** 8 720 000

10. 2.65×10^2	**13.** 1.9×10^{-2}	**16.** 8.5×10^{-4}
11. 1.8×10^{-1}	**14.** 7.67×10^4	**17.** 7×10^3
12. 3.02×10^3	**15.** 3.9×10^5	**18.** 4×10^{-3}

19. 5.87×10^4	**22.** 7×10^{-6}	**25.** 2.4×10^4
20. 2.6×10^3	**23.** 8×10^{-1}	**26.** 3.9×10^7
21. 4.5×10^5	**24.** 5.6×10^{-4}	**27.** 8×10^{-11}

28. a) 6.25×10^{10} b) 6.6049×10^8
c) 6.4×10^{-9} d) 4.9×10^{-11}

EXERCISE 1l   Deals with decimal places and significant figures and should be revised before later work involving use of calculators, in Chapters 19, 20 and 21.

1. a) 2.785	**3.** a) 3.209	**5.** a) 0.151
b) 2.78	b) 3.21	b) 0.151
2. a) 0.157	**4.** a) 0.073	**6.** a) 0.020
b) 0.157	b) 0.0733	b) 0.0204

7. a) 0.780	**9.** a) 254.163	**11.** a) 7.820
b) 0.780	b) 254	b) 7.82
8. a) 3.299	**10.** a) 0.001	**12.** a) 0.010
b) 3.30	b) 0.000 926	b) 0.009 64

13. 0.04; 0.0384	**16.** 80; 69.8
14. 60 000; 47 500	**17.** 0.2; 0.216
15. 0.05; 0.0447	**18.** 500 000; 665 000

19. 2; 2.17	**22.** 0.0; 0.0688
20. 0.2; 0.217	**23.** 5; 4.58
21. 9; 8.89	**24.** 6; 5.38

25. 60; 56.0

26. 0.04; 0.0390

27. 80; 69.3

28. 0.03; 0.0328

29. 2; 1.74

30. 0.06; 0.0403

31. 0.1; 0.105

EXERCISE 1m This section introduces the number line and the open and closed circle notation. For Numbers 1–20 we suggest that the number line is drawn once and the ranges placed below the line. In Numbers 21–40 the pupils are asked to draw a number line for each question—this takes a considerable time if they are drawn accurately and scaled. It is sensible to encourage rough sketches here.

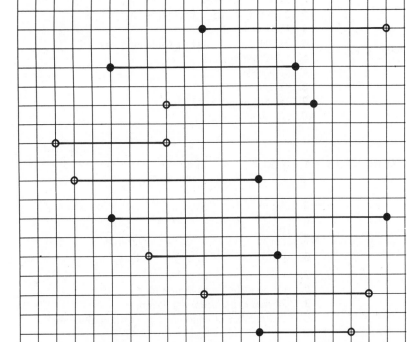

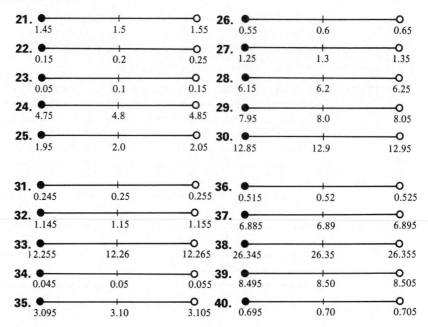

EXERCISE 1n
1. $5.55 \leqslant w < 5.65$
2. $2450 \leqslant x < 2550$
3. $2.75 \leqslant x < 2.85$
4. $12.45 \leqslant x < 12.55$
5. $74\,500 \leqslant x \leqslant 75\,499$ (whole numbers only)
6. $1.245 \leqslant d < 1.255$
7. 65 people
8. £54.995
9. $252.5 \leqslant$ length < 257.5
10. $97.5\,m$

EXERCISE 1p
1. a) 30   b) 42
2. a) $\frac{4}{3}$ b) $\frac{y}{x}$
3. a) $\frac{3}{2}$ b) $\frac{4}{9}$
4. $2\frac{3}{10}$
5. a) 3.36   b) 0.2943   c) 109
6. a) 16   b) 1   c) $\frac{1}{16}$
7. a) 5^2 b) 5^{12}
8. a) 2.56×10^3 b) 2.56×10^{-4}
9. $1.45\,mm \leqslant$ diameter $< 1.55\,mm$
10. $65 \leqslant$ number of children $\leqslant 74$ (whole numbers)

EXERCISE 1q
  1. a) 24   b) 30
  2. a) 5   b) $\frac{2}{3}$
  3. a) $\frac{3}{4}$ b) $1\frac{17}{20}$
  4. a) $3\frac{1}{12}$
  5. a) 1.45   b) 2.625   c) 0.42
  6. a) $\frac{1}{4}$ b) 1   c) 4
  7. a) 5.7×10^{5} b) 5.7×10^{-2}
  8. $445 \leqslant$ number of tacks $\leqslant 454$ (whole numbers)
  9. $0.745\,\text{m} \leqslant$ diameter $< 0.755\,\text{m}$

CHAPTER 2   Equations, Inequalities and Formulae

The first part of this chapter revises directed numbers, collection of like terms, and solution of linear equations.

EXERCISE 2a   Can be used as a quick reminder of directed numbers.

1. >	**3.** <	**5.** <
2. <	**4.** >	**6.** <

7. -2	**9.** 3	**11.** -4
8. -11	**10.** 1	**12.** 0

13. -8	**16.** 12	**19.** -2
14. -2	**17.** -8	**20.** 48
15. 4	**18.** 2	**21.** 35

EXERCISE 2b   Simplification of algebraic expressions, including practice in the use of directed numbers.

1. Not possible	**6.** $p+q$
2. $2a$	**7.** $4x-2y$
3. Not possible	**8.** $5u$
4. $7v$	**9.** $3b-a$
5. $2x$	**10.** $4c+2d$

EXERCISE 2c
1. xy	**5.** $\dfrac{u}{v}$
2. a^2	**6.** $\dfrac{-a}{b}$
3. $6s^2$	**7.** 1
4. $12x^2$	**8.** $\dfrac{3b}{c}$

9. Not possible

10. Not possible

11. $-mn$

12. Not possible

13. $-2a$

14. $4p^3$

15. $\dfrac{2u}{w}$

16. Not possible

17. $6st$

18. $2p^2$

19. $-4q$

20. $r+4s$

21. $\dfrac{4p}{q}$

22. $6st$

23. $-2b^2$

24. $\dfrac{x}{y}$

25. $3b-2a$

26. a^2-a

27. $3a-3b$

28. $6a-4c-2b$

29. $2z-y$

30. $6x+4y+2z$

31. $p+3q-2r$

32. $x-y$

33. $5q-p$

34. $a^2+ab-2a+2b$

35. x^2+y^2-2xy

36. $2b-6c$

37. $2p-2q$

38. w^2+x^2

39. $8n-2m$

40. $2b-8c$

EXERCISE 2d   Can be used for discussion and as a reminder about the meaning of "equation" before beginning the work on inequalities.

1. $p=-\frac{2}{3}$

2. $s=\frac{1}{2}$

3. $x=3\frac{1}{2}$

4. $a=\frac{1}{5}$

5. $x=1$

6. $y=1$

7. $x=2$

8. $a=4$

9. $x=\frac{1}{2}$

10. $x=2$

11. $x=-\frac{1}{2}$

12. $x=-5$

13. $x=-\frac{1}{7}$

14. $y=3\frac{1}{3}$

15. $x=2\frac{4}{7}$

16. $x=3\frac{2}{3}$

17. $a=-11$

18. $p=0$

19. $w=2$

20. $x=5$

21. $x=6\frac{1}{2}$

22. $x=-\frac{1}{6}$

23. $x=2\frac{1}{2}$

24. $x=1\frac{3}{4}$

25. $x=\frac{3}{14}$

26. $b=19$

27. $x=\frac{5}{6}$

28. $x=-1$

29. $x=2$

30. $x=\frac{1}{2}$

EXERCISE 2e   Work in Exercise 1m should be discussed before this section. Numbers 10–15 can be used for discussion.

1. 7

2. 4

3. -2

4. 0

5. -2

6. $\frac{1}{2}$

7. 5

8. 0

9. 1.5

10. a) $2,3,4,6,7$ b) $2,5,7,8,9$ c) $2,3,7,9$
    d) $2,3,4,6,7$ e) $2,3,4,7,9$

12. a) $5>3$; Yes   b) $1>-1$; Yes
    c) $-2>-4$; Yes   d) $7>5$; Yes

13. a) $0 > -1$; Yes   b) $-4 > -5$; Yes
    c) $-7 > -8$; Yes   d) $2 > 1$; Yes
14. a) $1 < b$; Yes   b) $-3 < 2$; Yes
    c) $-6 < -1$; Yes   d) $3 < 8$; Yes

EXERCISE 2f   Numbers 28–32 can be used for discussion.

1. $x < 12$ (12)   **6.** $x < 3$ (3)

2. $x < 2$ (2)   **7.** $x < -3$ (−3)

3. $x > 5$ (5)   **8.** $x < -7$ (−7)

4. $x > 2$ (2)   **9.** $x < -5$ (−5)

5. $x < -2$ (−2)

10. $x < -2$ (−2)   **15.** $x < -3$ (−3)

11. $x > -1$ (−1)   **16.** $x < 1$ (1)

12. $x < 3$ (3)   **17.** $x > -2$ (−2)

13. $x > 0$ (0)   **18.** $x < -5$ (−5)

14. $x > -3$ (−3)

19. $x < 5$ (5)   **24.** $x > -5$ (−5)

20. $x < 1$ (1)   **25.** $x > -3$ (−3)

21. $x < -1$ (−1)   **26.** $x < 13$ (13)

22. $x > 0$ (0)   **27.** $x > 12$ (12)

23. $x > 7$ (7)

28. a) $24 < 72$ b) $3 < 9$ c) $6 < 18$
    d) $2 < 6$ e) $-24 < -72$ f) $-4 < -12$
    a) Yes   b) Yes   c) Yes   d) Yes   e) No   f) No

29. a) $72 > -24$ b) $9 > -3$ c) $18 > -6$
    d) $6 > -2$ e) $-72 > 24$ f) $-12 > 4$
    a) Yes   b) Yes   c) Yes   d) Yes   e) No   f) No

30. a) $-36 < -12$ b) $-4\frac{1}{2} < -1\frac{1}{2}$ c) $-9 < -3$
    d) $-3 < -1$ e) $36 < 12$ f) $9 < 2$
    a) Yes   b) Yes   c) Yes   d) Yes   e) No   f) No

32. Only when you are multiplying by a positive number.

EXERCISE 2g

1. ———○ $x < 3$
         3

2. ○——— $x > 1$
    1

3. ○——— $x > 2$
    2

4. ———○ $x < 1$
         1

5. ———○ $x < \frac{1}{2}$
         $\frac{1}{2}$

6. ○——— $x > 1\frac{1}{3}$
    $1\frac{1}{3}$

7. ———○ $x < 2\frac{1}{4}$
         $2\frac{1}{4}$

8. ○——— $x > 1\frac{1}{2}$
    $1\frac{1}{2}$

9. ———● $x \leqslant 1$
         1

10. ———● $x \leqslant 4$
         4

11. ●——— $x \geqslant -2$
   -2

12. ●——— $x \geqslant 1$
    1

13. ———○ $x < -1$
        -1

14. ———● $x \leqslant 2$
         2

15. ○——— $x > 1$
    1

16. ●——— $x \geqslant 1\frac{1}{3}$
   $1\frac{1}{3}$

17. ●——— $x \geqslant 0$
    0

18. ———● $x \leqslant 1$
         1

19. ———○ $x < 1$
         1

20. ———○ $x < -3$
        -3

21. a) $x > 3$ b) $2 \leqslant x \leqslant 3$
       c) No values of x

22. a) $0 \leqslant x \leqslant 1$ b) $x \leqslant 0$
       c) No values of x

23. a) $-2 < x \leqslant 4$ b) No values of x
       c) $x < -2$

24. a) $-3 < x; \; -1$ b) $x < -3$
       c) No values of x

25. $x < 12; \; x > -1; \; -1 < x < 12$
26. $x \leqslant -1; \; x \geqslant 3; \;$ No values of x
27. $x \leqslant 7; \; x \geqslant -2; \; -2 \leqslant x \leqslant 7$
28. $x > 1; \; x < 2; \; 1 < x < 2$

29. $x > 2; \; x < 3; \; 2 < x < 3$
30. $x < 2; \; x > -1; \; -1 < x < 2$
31. $x \geqslant -1; \; x < 2; \; -1 \leqslant x < 2$

32. $x > \frac{1}{2}; \; x \leqslant 3; \; \frac{1}{2} < x \leqslant 3$

33. $2 < x < 5$
34. $-3 \leqslant x \leqslant 2$
35. $x < -2$
36. $x < 0$
37. $x \geqslant 1$

38. $-4 < x < 2$
39. $x < -3$
40. $x < -1$
41. $1\frac{4}{5} < x < 3$
42. $\frac{1}{2} < x < 1$

EXERCISE 2h   These problems are slightly harder than those in Book 2. A general discussion on units is advisable and Numbers 11–20 can be used for this purpose, although the most able pupils can work through these on their own.

1. $a = b + c$

2. $m = 2(n + p)$

3. $z = xy$

4. $a = 2bc$

5. $v = n^2$

6. $d = e - f$

7. $x = \dfrac{y}{2}$

8. $a = \dfrac{b}{2c}$

9. $k = 2u + 3v$

10. $x = 2y - z$

11. $n = p + p^2$

12. $v = u + at$

13. $R = Np$

14. $y = nx$

15. $X = xy$

16. $N = y + z$

17. $P = \dfrac{x + y}{50}$

18. $b = \dfrac{ac}{1000}$

19. $n = 1 + 2m$

20. $R = \dfrac{x}{10} + \dfrac{y}{5}$

EXERCISE 2i   Gives more practice in the use of directed numbers.

1. $p = 8$

2. $v = 2$

3. $z = \frac{3}{4}$

4. $a = 2$

5. $x = 25$

6. $C = 30$

7. $x = 24$

8. $p = 6$

9. $S = 10$

10. $v = -5$

11. $p = 4$

12. $a = 9$

13. $r = 2\frac{2}{3}$

14. $n = \frac{1}{2}$

15. $a = 2$

16. $V = 32$

17. $p = 21$

18. $a = 6$

EXERCISE 2j   Numbers 1–20 require one operation. Numbers 21–36 require two operations. Some of these involve division of, say, $x + y$ by another letter or number. It is a good idea to encourage the use of brackets in this situation, e.g. $2a = x + y$, $2a = (x + y)$, $a = \dfrac{(x + y)}{2}$.

1. $s = p - r$

2. $y = x - 3$

3. $b = a + c$

4. $Y = X + Z$

5. $s = r - 2t$

6. $m = k - l$

7. $v = u + 5$

8. $y = z - x$

9. $P = N + Q$

10. $u = v - 10t$

11. $y = \dfrac{x}{2}$

12. $t = 2v$

13. $b = \dfrac{a}{c}$

14. $u = 3t$

15. $m = kl$

16. $b = \dfrac{a}{3}$

17. $N = 10X$

18. $u = \dfrac{v}{t}$

19. $w = 100z$

20. $p = qn$

21. $s = \dfrac{P-r}{2}$

22. $t = \dfrac{u-v}{3}$

23. $c = \dfrac{b-a}{4}$

24. $v = \dfrac{V-3u}{2}$

25. $w = \dfrac{x+y}{2}$

26. $t = \dfrac{l-k}{4}$

27. $y = \dfrac{x-w}{6}$

28. $s = \dfrac{It-N}{2}$

29. $y = \dfrac{4x}{3}$

30. $t = \dfrac{u-v}{5}$

31. $I = 10(A-P)$

32. $y = 3(x-z)$

33. $R = \dfrac{IV}{2}$

34. $r = \dfrac{p+w}{2}$

35. $c = 2(a-b)$

36. $r = 5(q-p)$

37. $u = v-at;\ u = 140$

38. $B = A - \dfrac{C}{100};\ B = 17.5$

39. $C = NP;\ C = 40$

40. $x = 2(z+3t);\ x = -10$

41. a) $a = b+2c$ b) $a = 4$ c) $b = a-2c$

42. a) $x = 2yz$ b) $x = 12$ c) $y = \dfrac{x}{2y}$

43. a) $d = e^2 + 2f$ b) $f = \dfrac{d-e^2}{2}$ c) $f = \tfrac{1}{2}$

44. a) $R = \dfrac{3xn}{25}$ b) $R = 4.8$

EXERCISE 2k

1. a) -4 b) -1 c) -2

2. a) $4x$ b) $6b$ c) $-3x^3$

3. a) $a+b$ b) $a+5b$

4. a) $x = 1\tfrac{1}{4}$ b) $x = 4\tfrac{2}{3}$

5. a) $x > 2$ b) $x \leqslant 6$ c) $-2 < x < 1\tfrac{1}{2}$

6. a) $r = \dfrac{v-u}{4}$ b) $r = \dfrac{ps}{5}$

7. a) $P = 37\tfrac{1}{2}$ b) 40

EXERCISE 2l

1. a) 13 b) 2 c) 4

2. a) $10a-3b$ b) $4x+x^2$ c) $12ab$

3. a) $3y-2x$ b) $2y-6x$

4. a) $a = -1$ b) $x = \tfrac{7}{8}$

5. a) $x > 1$ b) $x > -1$ c) $-1 < x < 1$

6. a) $d = \dfrac{C}{\pi}$ b) $d = \dfrac{a+s}{7}$

7. a) $u = 56$ b) $u = -86$

CHAPTER 3   Congruent Triangles

In this chapter a movement starts towards a more formal and non-numerical treatment of geometry, although the emphasis throughout this book is still on the intuitive recognition of facts. The first section revises the basic facts and begins the progression towards a reasoned answer. The proof that the sum of the interior angles of a triangle is 180° can be used to demonstrate what can be reasoned from a few known facts. It can also be used to demonstrate what is acceptable as a reason.

The next section is an intuitive approach to congruency. After this the emphasis is on reasoned answers. The last part of this chapter contains a large number of non-numerical questions where a logical "proof" is essential. The less able children will find these difficult, so be cautious in allowing them to work on their own.

We have not included symmetry as a justification for saying that angles or sides are equal, but the teacher may decide that, where appropriate, it is an acceptable reason.

Geometry is put on a formal basis in Book 4A with an introduction to the deductive nature of Euclidian Geometry.

EXERCISE 3a   Numbers 9–13 are non-numerical and several examples should be used for discussion before pupils attempt them on their own. It is sensible to accept, as reasons, any facts that they know, e.g. in Number 4 they may use the fact that opposite angles of a parallelogram are equal. Some discussion is also necessary on naming angles when there is more than one angle at a vertex. Either the angle must be clearly marked on the diagram with a small letter or three letters have to be used.

1. 70°		**5.** 45°	
2. 110°		**6.** 55°	
3. 60°		**7.** 125°	
4. 70°		**8.** 66°	

EXERCISE 3b

1. Yes	**6.** No
2. No	**7.** Yes
3. Yes	**8.** No
4. No	**9.** Yes
5. Yes	**10.** Yes

EXERCISE 3c

1. Reflection in x-axis; Yes
2. Rotation of 90° anticlockwise about 0; Yes
3. Enlargement, scale factor 2, centre $(-4, 0)$; No
4. Translation $\begin{pmatrix} -3 \\ -2 \end{pmatrix}$; Yes
5. Reflection in y-axis; Yes
6. Enlargement, scale factor $\frac{1}{2}$, centre $(0, 0)$; No
7. Rotation of 90° clockwise about $(5, 2)$; Yes
8. Translation $\begin{pmatrix} -3 \\ -2 \end{pmatrix}$; Yes

EXERCISE 3d   **1.** $B\hat{A}C = 38.7°$, $A\hat{B}C = 51.3°$, $A\hat{C}B = 90°$; Yes
2. No
3. $B\hat{A}C = 106°$, $A\hat{B}C = 39.9°$. $A\hat{C}B = 34.1°$; Yes
4. No
5. The length of one side

EXERCISE 3e   **1.** Yes; SSS   **4.** No
2. No   **5.** No
3. No   **6.** Yes; SSS

7. Yes   **9.** Yes
8. $\triangle ABC$ and $\triangle ADC$ **10.** Yes

EXERCISE 3f   **5.** Two are: $\triangle ABC$ and $\triangle LMN$
6. Two

EXERCISE 3g   **1.** Yes; AAS   **6.** Yes; AAS
2. No; similar   **7.** Yes; AAS
3. Yes; AAS   **8.** No
4. Yes; AAS   **9.** Yes
5. No   **10.** Yes

EXERCISE 3h   **1.** Yes; $AC = 4.4$ cm, $\hat{A} = 34.3°$, $\hat{C} = 115.7°$
2. No
3. Yes; $PR = 7.2$ cm, $\hat{R} = 46°$, $\hat{P} = 74°$
4. No
5. Yes; $DF = 7.8$ cm, $D = 50°$, $F = 40°$

EXERCISE 3i   After this exercise has been completed it is sensible to discuss when knowing two sides and a non-included angle of a triangle gives a unique triangle and when it doesn't.

1. Yes
2. No; there are two possibilities
3. Yes
4. No; there are two possibilities
5. Yes
6. Yes
7. In questions 1, 3 and 5 we can calculate the length of the third side.

EXERCISE 3j   Here is a practical application of congruent triangles:
This is a way of finding the width of a river without having to cross it. Put a stake A in the ground on one bank opposite a bush or tree B on the other bank. Walk along the bank at right angles to AB for a reasonable distance and put in another stake C. Carry on walking in the same straight line until you have covered a distance equal to AC. Put in another stake D. Now walk at right angles to AD

until you are in a straight line with BC. Place another stake E. DE is the width of the river.

Draw a diagram illustrating this and explain why it works.

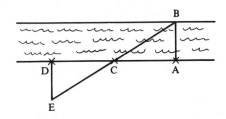

1. Yes; SAS
2. Not necessarily
3. Yes; SHR
4. Yes; SAS
5. Yes; SAS

6. Not necessarily
7. Yes; SHR
8. Not necessarily
9. Yes; SHR
10. Yes

EXERCISE 3k

1. No
2. Yes; AAS
3. Yes; SSS
4. Yes; AAS
5. No

6. Yes; SAS
7. No; similar
8. Yes; ASS
9. Yes; SHR
10. Yes; SSS

11. Yes; ASS
12. Yes; SAS
13. No
14. No; similar
15. Yes; SHR

EXERCISE 3l   9. △BDF and △CDE

EXERCISE 3m Only for the most able children.

EXERCISE 3n This provides useful extra practice on congruent triangles but can be omitted.

1. AC bisects both angles; Yes
2. Both are right angles
3. No
4. They are equal
5. Yes; No; Yes, of AC; they are all right angles
6. No
7. They are equal

EXERCISE 3p If Exercise 3n was not covered, a reminder of the properties of special quadrilaterals is needed before this exercise is attempted. It includes several numerical and constructional questions. Remind pupils that "construct" means "make an accurate drawing of".

1. 5 cm
2. 5 cm
3. 60°

5. 8 cm
6. 5 cm
7. 9.5 cm

8. 6 cm
9. 5.7 cm

CHAPTER 4   Matrices

EXERCISE 4a
1. 2×2
2. 2×3
3. 2×1
4. 1×3
5. 1×1
6. 3×2

7. a) 6   b) 8   c) 2   d) 7

8. 3 1 7; $\begin{matrix} 4 \\ 7 \\ 2 \end{matrix}$ a) 7   b) 6   c) 4

9. $\begin{pmatrix} 0 & 0 & 0 \\ 1 & 1 & 1 \\ 2 & 2 & 2 \end{pmatrix}$

10. $\begin{pmatrix} 3 & 1 \\ 3 & 1 \\ 3 & 1 \end{pmatrix}$

EXERCISE 4b
1. $\begin{pmatrix} 12 \\ 15 \end{pmatrix}$

2. $\begin{pmatrix} 15 & 4 \\ 7 & 1 \end{pmatrix}$

3. Not possible

4. (9, 5)

5. $\begin{pmatrix} 11 & 2 & 2 \\ 6 & 7 & 7 \end{pmatrix}$

6. $\begin{pmatrix} 11 & 11 \\ 11 & 5 \end{pmatrix}$

7. (5 3 5)

8. Not possible

9. $\begin{pmatrix} 6 & 8 \\ 7 & 7 \\ 7 & 7 \end{pmatrix}$

10. (10 8)

11. $\begin{pmatrix} 1 & 8 \\ -4 & 7 \end{pmatrix}$

12. $\begin{pmatrix} -2 \\ 2 \end{pmatrix}$

13. $\begin{pmatrix} -2 & 7 \\ -5 & 3 \end{pmatrix}$

14. (4 6)

15. $\begin{pmatrix} -3 \\ -3 \\ 6 \end{pmatrix}$

16. Not possible

17. $\begin{pmatrix} 2 & 10 \\ 5 & -3 \end{pmatrix}$

18. $\begin{pmatrix} 5 & -5 \\ 3 & 0 \end{pmatrix}$

19. $\begin{pmatrix} 0 & 8 \\ 8 & -2 \end{pmatrix}$

20. Not possible

21. Not possible
22. (1 6 −3)

23. $\begin{pmatrix} 2 & 3 & 4 \\ 5 & 0 & -12 \end{pmatrix}$

EXERCISE 4c
1. $\begin{pmatrix} 3 \\ 6 \\ 12 \end{pmatrix}$

2. $\begin{pmatrix} 2 & 8 & 0 \\ 4 & -2 & 6 \end{pmatrix}$

3. $\begin{pmatrix} 1 & 2 \\ \frac{1}{2} & 3 \\ 1\frac{1}{2} & 4 \end{pmatrix}$

5. $\begin{pmatrix} -6 & -30 \\ 6 & 12 \end{pmatrix}$

4. $\begin{pmatrix} 6 & 24 \\ 18 & -12 \end{pmatrix}$

6. $\begin{pmatrix} 4 & 0 \\ \frac{2}{3} & 1\frac{1}{3} \\ 2 & 3\frac{1}{3} \end{pmatrix}$

7. $\begin{pmatrix} 2 & -2 \\ 1 & 3 \end{pmatrix}$

10. $\begin{pmatrix} 2 & 4 & 2 \\ -3 & -3 & -1 \end{pmatrix}$

8. Not possible

11. Not possible

9. $\begin{pmatrix} -3 \\ 3 \\ 0 \end{pmatrix}$

12. $\begin{pmatrix} -3 & -1 & 2 \\ 9 & 5 & 4 \\ 1 & 11 & 5 \end{pmatrix}$

EXERCISE 4d   **1.** $\begin{pmatrix} -1 & 8 \\ 6 & 1 \end{pmatrix}$

7. $\begin{pmatrix} 2 & 8 \\ 6 & 4 \end{pmatrix}$

2. $\begin{pmatrix} 3 & 0 \\ 0 & 3 \end{pmatrix}$

8. $\begin{pmatrix} -1 & 2 \\ 1\frac{1}{2} & -\frac{1}{2} \end{pmatrix}$

3. Not possible

9. $\begin{pmatrix} 8 \\ 9 \\ 3 \end{pmatrix}$

4. $\begin{pmatrix} 1 & -1 \\ 5 & -1 \end{pmatrix}$

10. $\begin{pmatrix} 24 & 8 & -4 \\ 16 & 12 & 16 \end{pmatrix}$

5. $\begin{pmatrix} 1\frac{1}{3} \\ 1\frac{2}{3} \\ -\frac{1}{3} \end{pmatrix}$

11. Not possible

6. $\begin{pmatrix} -3 \\ -3 \\ -3 \end{pmatrix}$

12. $\begin{pmatrix} 8 & -2 & -2 \\ 1 & 4 & 4 \end{pmatrix}$

EXERCISE 4e   A vector can be represented by a column matrix. Capital letters are used to denote matrices, including 2×1 column matrices, e.g. $\mathbf{A} = \begin{pmatrix} 1 \\ 4 \end{pmatrix}$, $\mathbf{B} = \begin{pmatrix} 5 & 2 \\ -4 & 3 \end{pmatrix}$, but a lower case letter is used when a column matrix represents a vector, e.g. $\mathbf{a} = \begin{pmatrix} 3 \\ -2 \end{pmatrix}$.

1. $\mathbf{B}$ 2×1, $\mathbf{C}$ 2×2, $\mathbf{D}$ 2×2, $\mathbf{E}$ 1×3, $\mathbf{F}$ 1×2, $\mathbf{G}$ 2×3

2. $\begin{pmatrix} 9 & 4 & 4 \\ 7 & 1 & 7 \end{pmatrix}$

6. Not possible

10. $\begin{pmatrix} 24 \\ 6 \end{pmatrix}$

3. Not possible

7. $(1\frac{1}{2} \ \ 1)$

11. $\begin{pmatrix} 4\frac{1}{2} & 1\frac{1}{2} \\ \frac{3}{4} & 3 \end{pmatrix}$

4. $\begin{pmatrix} 4 & -1 \\ 0 & 6 \end{pmatrix}$

8. Not possible

12. Not possible

5. $\begin{pmatrix} 12 & 9 & 3 \\ 3 & 6 & 9 \end{pmatrix}$

9. $\begin{pmatrix} 1 & -2 & 2 \\ 5 & -3 & 1 \end{pmatrix}$

13. Not possible

EXERCISE 4f   Here are two methods for remembering the order of matrix multiplication: (1) Calling the process "row–column" multiplication helps emphasise that rows are taken from the first matrix and columns from the second. (2) The picture of a person running along a diving board and then diving downwards gives the idea of "row first and then column".

1. $\begin{pmatrix} 29 \\ 27 \end{pmatrix}$ **4.** $\begin{pmatrix} 9 \\ 2 \end{pmatrix}$ **7.** $\begin{pmatrix} 26 \\ 10 \end{pmatrix}$ **9.** $\begin{pmatrix} 56 \\ 49 \end{pmatrix}$

2. $\begin{pmatrix} 14 \\ 11 \end{pmatrix}$ **5.** $\begin{pmatrix} 9 \\ 5 \end{pmatrix}$ **8.** $\begin{pmatrix} 58 \\ 19 \end{pmatrix}$ **10.** $\begin{pmatrix} 26 \\ 10 \end{pmatrix}$

3. $\begin{pmatrix} 5 \\ 7 \end{pmatrix}$ **6.** $\begin{pmatrix} 18 \\ 14 \end{pmatrix}$

EXERCISE 4g   **1.** $\begin{pmatrix} 7 \\ 10 \end{pmatrix}$ **5.** $\begin{pmatrix} 19 \\ 22 \end{pmatrix}$

2. $\begin{pmatrix} 14 \\ & 22 \end{pmatrix}$ **6.** $\begin{pmatrix} & 16 \\ 12 \end{pmatrix}$

3. $\begin{pmatrix} & 37 \\ & 2 \end{pmatrix}$ **7.** $\begin{pmatrix} & 12 \\ & 3 \end{pmatrix}$

4. $\begin{pmatrix} 23 & 16 \end{pmatrix}$ **8.** $\begin{pmatrix} 17 & 19 \\ 5 \end{pmatrix}$

9. $\begin{pmatrix} 22 & 52 \\ 10 & 22 \end{pmatrix}$ **12.** $\begin{pmatrix} 8 & 18 \\ 18 & 36 \end{pmatrix}$

10. $\begin{pmatrix} 44 & 32 \\ 8 & 7 \end{pmatrix}$ **13.** $\begin{pmatrix} 44 & 40 \\ 18 & 31 \end{pmatrix}$

11. $\begin{pmatrix} 16 & 14 \\ 11 & 14 \end{pmatrix}$ **14.** $\begin{pmatrix} 21 & 7 \\ 17 & 9 \end{pmatrix}$

15. $\begin{pmatrix} 0 & 14 \\ 10 & 8 \end{pmatrix}$ **18.** $\begin{pmatrix} -24 & -17 \\ -10 & -9 \end{pmatrix}$

16. $\begin{pmatrix} 15 & 20 \\ 5 & 0 \end{pmatrix}$ **19.** $\begin{pmatrix} 21 & 11 \\ 9 & 2 \end{pmatrix}$

17. $\begin{pmatrix} 3 & -4 \\ 13 & 6 \end{pmatrix}$ **20.** $\begin{pmatrix} -16 & 1 \\ -6 & -1 \end{pmatrix}$

EXERCISE 4h   **1.** $\begin{pmatrix} 20 & 13 \\ 8 & 5 \end{pmatrix}$ **4.** $\begin{pmatrix} 44 & 29 \\ 6 & 4 \end{pmatrix}$ **7.** $\begin{pmatrix} 15 & 17 \\ 31 & 35 \end{pmatrix}$ **10.** $\begin{pmatrix} 4 & 2 \\ 8 & 6 \end{pmatrix}$

2. $\begin{pmatrix} 10 & 7 \\ 22 & 15 \end{pmatrix}$ **5.** $\begin{pmatrix} 8 & 6 \\ 4 & 2 \end{pmatrix}$ **8.** $\begin{pmatrix} 46 & 31 \\ 6 & 4 \end{pmatrix}$ **11.** $\begin{pmatrix} 14 & 16 \\ 2 & 2 \end{pmatrix}$

3. $\begin{pmatrix} 31 & 35 \\ 15 & 17 \end{pmatrix}$ **6.** $\begin{pmatrix} 8 & 6 \\ 4 & 2 \end{pmatrix}$ **9.** $\begin{pmatrix} 4 & 2 \\ 8 & 6 \end{pmatrix}$ **12.** $\begin{pmatrix} 14 & 16 \\ 2 & 2 \end{pmatrix}$

13. One of the two matrices was **D**

EXERCISE 4i

1. $\begin{pmatrix} 7 \\ 10 \end{pmatrix}$

3. (10)

2. $\begin{pmatrix} 13 \\ 32 \end{pmatrix}$

4. $\begin{pmatrix} 20 & 10 \\ 70 & 23 \end{pmatrix}$

5. $\begin{pmatrix} 32 & 26 & 16 \\ 20 & 19 & 11 \end{pmatrix}$

8. $\begin{pmatrix} 10 & 11 \\ 36 & 30 \\ 31 & 28 \end{pmatrix}$

6. $\begin{pmatrix} 24 \\ 33 \\ 42 \end{pmatrix}$

9. $\begin{pmatrix} 21 & 39 & 8 \\ 17 & 26 & 7 \end{pmatrix}$

7. $(13 \ \ 31 \ \ 27)$

10. (15)

EXERCISE 4j

1. $2 \times \boxed{2 \ \ 2} \times 1 = 2 \times 1; \begin{pmatrix} 7 \\ 6 \end{pmatrix}$

5. $2 \times \boxed{2 \ \ 2} \times 2 = 2 \times 2; \begin{pmatrix} 11 & 20 \\ 24 & 43 \end{pmatrix}$

2. $2 \times \boxed{3 \ \ 3} \times 1 = 2 \times 1; \begin{pmatrix} 22 \\ 12 \end{pmatrix}$

6. $2 \times \boxed{1 \ \ 1} \times 2 = 2 \times 2; \begin{pmatrix} 3 & 4 \\ 6 & 8 \end{pmatrix}$

3. $1 \times \boxed{2 \ \ 2} \times 1 = 1 \times 1; (10)$

7. $1 \times \boxed{2 \ \ 2} \times 2 = 1 \times 2; (21 \ \ 36)$

4. $2 \times \boxed{3 \ \ 3} \times 2 = 2 \times 2; \begin{pmatrix} 20 & 10 \\ 70 & 23 \end{pmatrix}$

8. $3 \times \boxed{1 \ \ 1} \times 3 = 3 \times 3; \begin{pmatrix} 4 & 5 & 6 \\ 8 & 10 & 12 \\ 12 & 15 & 18 \end{pmatrix}$

9. $\begin{pmatrix} 16 \\ 6 \end{pmatrix}$

14. Not possible

10. Not possible

15. (30)

11. $\begin{pmatrix} 11 & 20 \\ 24 & 43 \end{pmatrix}$

16. Not possible

12. Not possible

17. $(3 \ \ 24)$

13. $\begin{pmatrix} 15 & 4 & 3 \\ 48 & 13 & 12 \end{pmatrix}$

18. $\begin{pmatrix} 6 & 12 & 15 \\ 8 & 16 & 20 \\ 2 & 4 & 5 \end{pmatrix}$

EXERCISE 4k

1. $\begin{pmatrix} 6 \\ 5 \end{pmatrix}$

6. $(-38 \ \ 12)$

2. $\begin{pmatrix} 10 \\ -19 \end{pmatrix}$

7. (-26)

3. $(-2 \ \ -6)$

8. $\begin{pmatrix} -24 & -4 & 12 \\ 6 & 1 & -3 \\ 6 & 1 & -3 \end{pmatrix}$

4. $\begin{pmatrix} 1 \\ 1 \\ -22 \end{pmatrix}$

9. $\begin{pmatrix} 7 & 18 & -1 \\ -7 & -18 & 1 \end{pmatrix}$

5. $\begin{pmatrix} 8 & -26 \\ -16 & -17 \end{pmatrix}$

10. $\begin{pmatrix} 12 & 18 \\ 8 & 12 \\ -6 & -9 \end{pmatrix}$

EXERCISE 4I

1. $\begin{pmatrix} 13 & -8 \\ 7 & -2 \end{pmatrix}$

2. $\begin{pmatrix} 2 & -1 \\ 12 & 9 \end{pmatrix}$

3. $\begin{pmatrix} 10 \\ 5 \end{pmatrix}$

4. Not possible

5. $\begin{pmatrix} 3 & 4 \\ 6 & 8 \end{pmatrix}$

6. Not possible

7. Not possible

8. Not possible

9. Not possible

10. (11)

11. (14 6)

12. Not possible

13. Not possible

14. (9 12)

15. Not possible

16. $AA = \begin{pmatrix} 19 & 18 \\ 6 & 7 \end{pmatrix}$ $AC = \begin{pmatrix} 21 & 8 \\ 4 & 2 \end{pmatrix}$ $BB = \begin{pmatrix} -5 & -2 \\ 3 & -6 \end{pmatrix}$

$BC = \begin{pmatrix} 8 & 2 \\ 18 & 6 \end{pmatrix}$ $BD = \begin{pmatrix} -3 \\ 3 \end{pmatrix}$ $CA = \begin{pmatrix} 26 & 22 \\ -4 & -3 \end{pmatrix}$

$CB = \begin{pmatrix} 12 & -12 \\ -1 & 2 \end{pmatrix}$ $CC = \begin{pmatrix} 34 & 12 \\ -6 & -2 \end{pmatrix}$ $CD = \begin{pmatrix} 10 \\ -1 \end{pmatrix}$

$DH = \begin{pmatrix} 3 \\ 6 \end{pmatrix}$ $EA = (16 \ 17)$ $EB = (15 \ -6)$

$FE = \begin{pmatrix} 18 & 24 \\ 3 & 4 \\ -12 & -16 \end{pmatrix}$ $FH = \begin{pmatrix} 18 \\ 3 \\ -12 \end{pmatrix}$ $GF = \begin{pmatrix} -4 \\ 15 \\ 5 \end{pmatrix}$

$GG = \begin{pmatrix} 18 & -2 & 17 \\ -13 & 35 & 11 \\ 23 & 4 & 27 \end{pmatrix}$ $HH = (9)$

EXERCISE 4m

1. $\begin{pmatrix} 8 & 2 \\ -21 & -8 \end{pmatrix}$

2. $\begin{pmatrix} 7 & 4 \\ -3 & 3 \end{pmatrix}$

3. $\begin{pmatrix} -5 & 0 \\ -5 & 3 \end{pmatrix}$

4. $\begin{pmatrix} 5 & 0 \\ 5 & -3 \end{pmatrix}$

5. Not possible

6. Not possible

7. $(-2 \ -3)$

8. $\begin{pmatrix} -2 & 1 \\ 8 & 12 \end{pmatrix}$

9. $\begin{pmatrix} 5 & 3 & 3 \\ 11 & 5 & 9 \\ 2 & 2 & 0 \end{pmatrix}$

10. Not possible

11. Not possible

12. (4 2)

EXERCISE 4n

1. $\begin{pmatrix} 12 & 10 \\ -2 & 13 \end{pmatrix}$

2. $\begin{pmatrix} 78 & -10 \\ 31 & -13 \end{pmatrix}$

3. $\begin{pmatrix} 13 & -6 \\ 18 & 1 \end{pmatrix}$

4. $\begin{pmatrix} 68 & 16 \\ 61 & 4 \end{pmatrix}$

5. $\begin{pmatrix} 48 & 40 \\ 38 & 17 \end{pmatrix}$

6. $\begin{pmatrix} 34 & -25 \\ 75 & -16 \end{pmatrix}$

7. $\begin{pmatrix} 78 & 8 \\ 31 & 28 \end{pmatrix}$

8. $\begin{pmatrix} 50 & 27 \\ 32 & 56 \end{pmatrix}$

9. $\begin{pmatrix} 55 & -11 \\ 66 & -22 \end{pmatrix}$

10. $\begin{pmatrix} -16 & 56 \\ -56 & 20 \end{pmatrix}$

11. $\begin{pmatrix} -64 & 0 \\ 0 & -64 \end{pmatrix}$

12. $\begin{pmatrix} 68 & -12 \\ 61 & -7 \end{pmatrix}$

EXERCISE 4p **1.** 2×2 and 2×1

2. Yes

3. **A, C** are compatible but not **C, A**

4. $\begin{pmatrix} 23 & -11 \\ 19 & -13 \end{pmatrix}$

5. $\mathbf{A}^2 = \begin{pmatrix} 27 & 18 \\ 9 & 18 \end{pmatrix}$.   It is not possible to find $\mathbf{C}^2$

6. Not possible

7. $\begin{pmatrix} 9 & -3 \\ 12 & -9 \end{pmatrix}$ **8.** $\begin{pmatrix} 13 & 3 \\ 6 & 5 \end{pmatrix}$ **9.** 4   **10.** **BC**

EXERCISE 4q **1.** $\begin{pmatrix} 4 & 2 & -2 \\ 8 & 6 & 2 \end{pmatrix}$

2. Not possible

3. Not possible

4. 2×3 and 2×2

5. No

6. 3

7. 1

8. **QP**

9. $\begin{pmatrix} 17 \\ 13 \end{pmatrix}$

10. $\mathbf{P}^2$ is not possible to find. $\mathbf{Q}^2 = \begin{pmatrix} 7 & 14 \\ -7 & 14 \end{pmatrix}$

CHAPTER 5 Percentages

For all but the best pupils, the early work in this chapter requires constant revision. The rest of this chapter concentrates on percentage increase and decrease in a variety of situations. It is the vocabulary and not the mathematics that often leads to difficulty here, so make sure that the pupils understand terms such as VAT, depreciation, percentage profit, etc.

EXERCISE 5a

	Fraction	Percentage	Decimal
1.	$\frac{3}{5}$	60%	0.6
2.	$\frac{2}{5}$	40%	0.4
3.	$\frac{11}{20}$	55%	0.55
4.	$\frac{17}{20}$	85%	0.85
5.	$\frac{27}{50}$	54%	0.54
6.	$\frac{6}{25}$	24%	0.24
7.	$\frac{23}{25}$	92%	0.92

Fraction	Percentage	Decimal
8. $\frac{21}{25}$	84%	0.84
9. $\frac{37}{40}$	$92\frac{1}{2}$%	0.925
10. $\frac{2}{3}$	$66\frac{2}{3}$%	$0.\dot{6}$

11. 24%   **14.** 40%   **17.** 5%   **20.** 27%
12. 64%   **15.** 25%   **18.** 2.5%   **21.** 40%
13. 20%   **16.** 34%   **19.** 2%   **22.** 225%

23. 75   **26.** 0.54 km   **29.** 2.5%   **32.** 2.5%
24. 92 p   **27.** 189 g   **30.** 2%   **33.** 2.4%
25. 0.61 cm   **28.** 42 m²   **31.** 1.5%

34. 60%   **37.** 949   **40.** 381   **42.** 348
35. 30%   **38.** 1007   **41.** 49.28   **43.** 31.59
36. 89.6%   **39.** 627

44. 172   **46.** 294   **48.** 59.4 kg   **50.** 102
45. 64.68   **47.** 5.74   **49.** £9675

EXERCISE 5b   Numbers 23–30: Many teachers may prefer to use the idea of a multiplying factor as a slight variation of Method 2 in the worked example.
i.e.   if the rate of VAT is 15%

$$\text{Purchase price} = \text{marked price} \times 1.15 \text{ or } \frac{115}{100}$$

The idea may be used in many problems on percentages.

1. 25%   **3.** 25%   **5.** 20%   **7.** 15%
2. 30%   **4.** 10%   **6.** 20%   **8.** 24%

9. £56   **12.** £18   **15.** £8   **18.** £16.20
10. £72   **13.** £27   **16.** £14.40   **19.** £14
11. £60.90   **14.** £80   **17.** £12

20. (b) by £8   **23.** £34.50   **27.** £690
21. (b) by 70 p   **24.** £73.60   **28.** £9.20
22. the same   **25.** £9.66   **29.** £11.96
          26. £43.70   **30.** £17.25

EXERCISE 5c   **1.** £1500   **4.** £3750   **7.** £3300   **11.** £1800
2. £2400   **5.** £1935   **8.** £2240   **12.** £2100
3. £1950   **6.** £2478   **9.** £4000   **13.** £3540
              10. £7680   **14.** £2112
                       15. £4270

16. £28
17. £92
18. £25.60
19. £58
20. £33.60

21. £38.25
22. £16.15
23. £14.30
24. £32.25
25. a) £12.20   b) £14.80

EXERCISE 5d More teaching effort is usually required with this topic than for most other percentage questions. Multiplying factors can also be used here.

1. £70
2. £40
3. £16
4. £6
5. £2.70

6. £32
7. £800
8. £900
9. £800
10. £20

11. £40
12. £80
13. £200
14. £18
15. £13.60

16. £50
17. £160
18. £17
19. £160
20. £2000

21. £120
22. £125
23. £260
24. £184
25. £92

26. £12
27. £650
28. £160
29. 850 cm³
30. 25 cm

EXERCISE 5e
1. £31 920
2. £13.69
3. $33\frac{1}{3}\%$

4. 40%
5. £1200
6. £37.50

7. 212.5 cm³
8. £172
9. 15 km/h

10. 44 275
11. a) £7.20 b) £6.60
12. £280

EXERCISE 5f
1. £32
2. £112
3. £284.70
4. £188.72
5. £162.50

6. £126
7. £201.60
8. £375.30
9. £500
10. £168.80

11. £440
12. 7 years
13. 6.5%
14. £300
15. 4%

16. a) £170.40
17. a) £200
18. a) 3 years

b) £392
b) £170
b) 5 years

c) £816.20
c) £360
c) 4 years

EXERCISE 5g
1. £42
2. £76.32
3. £103.88

4. £191.77
5. £143.99
6. £206.72

7. £252.68
8. £48 400
9. £76

10. £1090
11. £12 800

CHAPTER 6 Straight Line Graphs

This chapter revises and slightly extends the work in Book 2. The diagrams for Exercise 6a can be done on squared paper as can some of the graphs in Exercise 6b, but graph paper should be used fairly soon so that values can be read more accurately.

EXERCISE 6a   **1.** $x = 4$ **2.** $y = 5$ **3.** $y = -3$ **4.** $x = -2$

5. 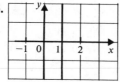   **6.**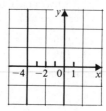

7. 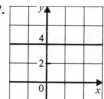   **8.**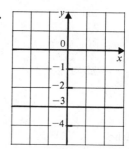

EXERCISE 6b   The graphs drawn for Numbers 5–8 are used for Numbers 17–20 so Numbers 17–20 can be done at the same time as Numbers 5–8.

1.

x	-2	0	4
y	2	4	8

3.

x	-3	0	3
y	7	4	1

2.

x	-2	0	3
y	-3	1	7

4.

x	-1	0	3
y	5	2	-4

13. a) $1\frac{1}{2}$ b) 0.4   c) -1.6
14. a) 0   b) -0.8 c) -3.4
15. a) -2.6 b) -1.8 c) 1.2
16. a) 3.6   b) 0.6   c) 1.2
17. a) $-2\frac{1}{2}$ b) 4.4   c) 2.4
18. a) 4.8   b) 1.2   c) -11.2
19. a) -1.4 b) 1.4   c) 3.5
20. a) 8.6   b) 2.8   c) 3

EXERCISE 6c   **1.** Yes, No   **4.** No, Yes
                   2. Yes, No   **5.** Yes, Yes
                   3. No, No   **6.** No, Yes

EXERCISE 6d   Squared paper can be used for this exercise.

    1. Lines are parallel; coefficient of x is 2 in each equation
    2. Lines are parallel; coefficient of x is -3 in each equation
    3. Lines are parallel; coefficient of x is $\frac{1}{2}$ in each equation
    4. Lines are parallel; coefficient of x is 1 in each equation
    5. Lines (a) and (c) are parallel
    6. Lines are parallel; coefficient of x is -1 in each equation

EXERCISE 6e   Squared paper can be used for this exercise. Number 8 provides another opportunity to emphasise that division by zero is not possible. In general, if a line is parallel to the y-axis avoid talking about its gradient.

    1. 4   **2.** -2 **3.** 1   **4.** $-\frac{3}{4}$ **5.** $-\frac{9}{5}$ **6.** $\frac{2}{3}$
    7. 0
    8. y-axis. You find yourself dividing by zero
    9. a) parallel to the y-axis   b) zero gradient
        c) zero gradient   d) parallel to the y-axis

EXERCISE 6f   **1.** 2   **2.** 1   **3.** 2   **4.** -2
    5. 4   **6.** a) 4   b) -3 c) 1   d) $\frac{1}{2}$

    7. a)

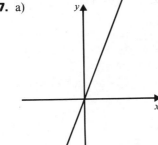

        b)

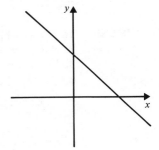

    8. a)

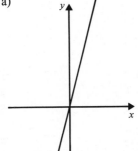

        b)

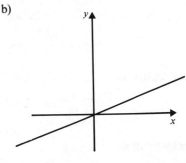

9. a) 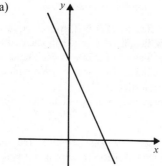   b)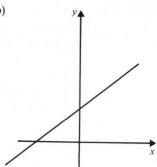

EXERCISE 6g

1. 2, 4	**4.** 1, -6	**7.** 5, 2	**11.** $-3, 7$
2. 5, 3	**5.** $-2, 3$	**8.** $\frac{1}{2}, -1$	**12.** $\frac{1}{3}, 7$
3. 3, -4	**6.** $-4, 2$	**9.** $-\frac{1}{3}, 4$	**13.** $-0.4, 9$
		10. 3, -7	**14.** 5, 4

15. 2, $2\frac{1}{2}$
16. $\frac{1}{3}, -2$
17. $\frac{2}{5}, 1$
18. $-\frac{3}{4}, 2$

19. $y = 2x + 7$
20. $y = 3x + 1$
21. $y = x + 3$
22. $y = 2x - 5$

23. $y = \frac{1}{2}x + 6$
24. $y = -2x + 1$
25. $y = x - 2$
26. $y = -\frac{1}{2}x + 4$

EXERCISE 6h

1. $y = 3x + 1$, $y = 5 + 3x$, $y = 3x - 4$
2. $y = 2 - x$, $y = 4 - x$, $2y = 3 - 2x$, $y = -x + 1$, $y = -x$
3. $3y = x$, $y = \frac{1}{3}x + 2$, $y = \frac{1}{3} + \frac{1}{3}x$, $y = \frac{1}{3}x - 4$
4. $y = \frac{1}{2}x + 2$ and $y = \frac{1}{2}x - 1$; $y = 2 - \frac{1}{2}x$ and $2y = 3 - x$
5. 2; $y = 2x + 3$
6. -3; $y = -3x + 1$
7. $y = 4x$
8. e.g. $y = 6 - x$, $y = -x$, $y = -2 - x$
9. a) $y = 4x + 4$ b) $y = -3x + 4$ c) $y = \frac{1}{2}x + 4$
10. a) $y = \frac{1}{3}x + 6$ b) $y = \frac{1}{3}x$ c) $y = \frac{1}{3}x - 3$
11. a) $y = 2x + 2$ b) $y = 2x + 10$ c) $y = 2x - 4$
12. $y = 3 + 2x$ and $y = 2x - 3$
13. $-3, 4$; $4, -3$; $y = -3x - 3$
14. a) $y = -4x$ b) $y = -4x - 7$

EXERCISE 6i

1. $-\frac{3}{5}$	**4.** -1	**7.** $\frac{1}{3}$
2. $-\frac{1}{3}$	**5.** -2	**8.** 2
3. $\frac{1}{4}$	**6.** $-\frac{1}{3}$	**9.** -1 in each case

EXERCISE 6j

1. $-\frac{3}{4}$	**3.** $\frac{1}{2}$	**5.** 2
2. $-\frac{3}{5}$	**4.** -2	**6.** $\frac{3}{4}$

7. a) $(2,0), (0,4)$ b) $(12,0), (0,-9)$

8. a) $\dfrac{x}{6} + \dfrac{y}{5} = 1$ b) $\dfrac{x}{4} - \dfrac{y}{3} = 1$

9. $-\dfrac{1}{3}$

EXERCISE 6k

1. $-\dfrac{3}{5}, 3$ **3.** $\dfrac{1}{4}, -2$ **5.** $3, 6$

2. $-\dfrac{1}{3}, 2$ **4.** $\dfrac{1}{3}, -2$ **6.** $-\dfrac{1}{3}, 2$

7. $-\dfrac{3}{4}, 3$ **10.** $-3, 6$ **13.** $4, 2$

8. $-\dfrac{3}{5}, 3$ **11.** $-\dfrac{4}{3}, 4$ **14.** $-1, 4$

9. $\dfrac{1}{2}, -2$ **12.** $\dfrac{4}{3}, -4$ **15.** $-2, 4$

16. $-\dfrac{2}{5}, 3$ **18.** $2, \dfrac{5}{2}$ **20.** $-1, -3$

17. $-\dfrac{1}{2}, 5$ **19.** $2, -4$ **21.** $-\dfrac{3}{4}, 3$

EXERCISE 6l

1. $-\dfrac{4}{3}, 4; \; y = -\dfrac{4}{3}x + 4$ **4.** $-\dfrac{4}{3}, 2; \; y = -\dfrac{4}{3}x + 2$

2. $-2, 7; \; y = -2x + 7$ **5.** $\dfrac{7}{2}, -4; \; y = \dfrac{7}{2}x - 4$

3. $\dfrac{3}{5}, 1; \; y = \dfrac{3}{5}x + 1$ **6.** $\dfrac{1}{3}, -1; \; y = \dfrac{1}{3}x - 1$

7. $\dfrac{1}{6}, 1; \; y = \dfrac{1}{6}x + 1$ **10.** $-1, -5; \; y = -x - 5$

8. $\dfrac{4}{5}, -3; \; y = \dfrac{4}{5}x - 3$ **11.** $2, 12; \; y = 2x + 12$

9. $\dfrac{5}{3}, -4; \; y = \dfrac{5}{3}x - 4$ **12.** $\dfrac{5}{6}, 6; \; y = \dfrac{5}{6}x + 6$

13. $AB, 5y = 2x + 20; \; AC, 5x + 3y = 12$

14. $3, \; y = 3x - 11$ **19.** $-1, \; y = -x + 3$

15. $-3, \; y = -3x + 7$ **20.** $-1, \; y = -x + 1$

16. $\dfrac{5}{2}, \; y = \dfrac{5}{2}x - \dfrac{1}{2}$ **21.** $2, \; y = 2x - 11$

17. $2, \; y = 2x + 7$ **22.** $\dfrac{1}{5}, \; y = \dfrac{1}{5}x - \dfrac{6}{5}$

18. $5, \; y = 5x - 21$ **23.** $-\dfrac{5}{2}, \; y = -\dfrac{5}{2}x + \dfrac{19}{2}$

24. $-\dfrac{5}{4}, \; \dfrac{x}{4} + \dfrac{y}{5} = 1 \;$ or $\; y = -\dfrac{5}{4}x + 5$

25. $-\dfrac{2}{3}, \; \dfrac{x}{3} + \dfrac{y}{2} = 1 \;$ or $\; y = -\dfrac{2}{3}x + 2$

26. $\dfrac{2}{3}, \; \dfrac{x}{3} - \dfrac{y}{2} = 1 \;$ or $\; y = \dfrac{2}{3}x - 2$

27. $-3, \; \dfrac{x}{2} + \dfrac{y}{6} = 1 \;$ or $\; y = -3x + 6$

28. $3, \; y = 3x - 10$ **30.** $-\dfrac{7}{2}, \; y = -\dfrac{7}{2}x - 6$

29. $-1, \; y = -x + 4$ **31.** $-1, \; y = -x + 3$

32. $\dfrac{5}{2}, \; -\dfrac{x}{2} + \dfrac{y}{5} = 1 \;$ or $\; y = \dfrac{5}{2}x + 5$

33. $\frac{2}{11}$, $y = \frac{2}{11}x + \frac{21}{11}$

34. 1, $y = x - 1$

35. $-\frac{1}{4}$, $y = -\frac{1}{4}x + \frac{11}{4}$

EXERCISE 6m
1. $y = 3x - 16$
2. Square
3. Rhombus
4. $(\frac{1}{2}, 3)$
5. Midpoint is $(5, 3)$; $y = -2x + 13$
6. $y = -x + 4$
7. Square

EXERCISE 6n
1. 2
2. $(0, 4)$
3. $(4, 0)$
4. 12
5. $y = 5x$
6. $(12, 0)$
7. Yes
8. $\frac{3}{5}$

EXERCISE 6p
1. -3
2. No
3. $y = -4x$
4. $(0, 4)$
5. $(0, 6), (6, 0)$
6. $-\frac{3}{2}$
7. $y = \frac{1}{2}x$
8. $(2, 0), (0, 3)$

CHAPTER 7   Simultaneous Equations

This chapter concentrates on solution by elimination. Matrix solution of simultaneous equations is in Chapter 8.

EXERCISE 7a
1. $3, 2$
2. $2, 4$
3. $3, 5$
4. $1, 7$
5. $4, -3$
6. $2, 5$
7. $-2, 1$
8. $5, 1$
9. $3, 1\frac{1}{2}$
10. $6, 0$
11. $-1, -2$
12. $0, 9$

EXERCISE 7b   When using addition to eliminate it is usually easier to eliminate the second letter, but common-sense is needed!

1. $3, 1$
2. $4, 2$
3. $3, 4$
4. $3, -1$
5. $3, \frac{1}{2}$
6. $9, 1$
7. $4, -2$
8. $1, 0$
9. $0, 6$
10. $2, 3$
11. $2, 3$
12. $4, -1$
13. $6, 2$
14. $5, 1\frac{1}{2}$
15. $4, 3$
16. $\frac{1}{2}, 4$
17. $4, -2$
18. $-3, 1$
19. $2, \frac{1}{3}$
20. $3, -2$

21. $3, 2$
22. $4, 5$
23. $3, 0$
24. $1\frac{1}{2}, 2$
25. $-3, 2$
26. $4, -2$
27. $6, 2$
28. $4, 3$
29. $-1, 4$
30. $-1, -2$
31. $5, 4$
32. $2, -4$

EXERCISE 7c
1. $3, 1$
2. $1, 2$
3. $\frac{1}{3}, 1$
4. $-12, 27$
5. $0, 1$
6. $4, 3$
7. $1, 2$
8. $2, 1$
9. $3, -1$
10. $0, 3$
11. $1, -1$
12. $3, \frac{1}{2}$

EXERCISE 7d

1. 3, 2	**5.** 0, 6	**9.** 2, 2	**13.** 2, $\frac{2}{3}$
2. 1, 5	**6.** 3, −1	**10.** 3, −1	**14.** −1, 2
3. 3, 1	**7.** 1, 4	**11.** 4, 2	**15.** 3, −2
4. $1\frac{1}{2}$, 0	**8.** 1, 1	**12.** −3, 0	**16.** 2, −2

17. 0, 4	**20.** 3, 1	**23.** −3, 4	**26.** 2, 5
18. −1, −2	**21.** 2, −1	**24.** 3, −$3\frac{1}{2}$	**27.** 3, 2
19. 1, 1	**22.** 8, 4	**25.** 3, 4	**28.** −1, −3

EXERCISE 7e

1. 1, 4	**6.** −1, −1
2. −1, 5	**7.** $3\frac{1}{2}$, $2\frac{1}{2}$
3. 3, −2	**8.** 1, −2
4. 6, 28	**9.** 5, 0
5. 2, 3	**10.** 0, 4

11. −1, −1	**12.** −4, −5

EXERCISE 7f Can be omitted.

1. 2, 4	**4.** −2, 7	**7.** 1, 10	**10.** −12, −4
2. 5, 3	**5.** 4, 6	**8.** $2\frac{1}{3}$, −$\frac{2}{3}$	**11.** 2, 6
3. 1, 1	**6.** 1, 1	**9.** 1, 5	**12.** $4\frac{1}{2}$, $7\frac{1}{2}$

EXERCISE 7h Most children find these difficult. Only the most able should work from Number 7 onwards on their own.

1. 12, 8	**4.** 10, 3
2. 11, 5	**5.** 10, 6
3. 8, 2	**6.** 11, 5

7. 3, 7	**11.** Harry 32, Adam 10, Sam 20
8. 54, 36	**12.** 3, 5
9. 60 p, 45 p	**13.** AB = $9\frac{1}{2}$ cm, BC = 6 cm
10. 25 p, 10 p	**14.** $m = 2$, $c = 4$, $y = 2x + 4$

EXERCISE 7i The graphical solution of linear simultaneous equations is not a satisfactory method (it takes too long) but the idea is needed later for solving non-linear equations. The use of graph paper is essential for this exercise as most of the solutions are fractional (integer solutions can often be spotted when the tables are being made).

1. $1\frac{1}{2}$, $4\frac{1}{2}$	**6.** $1\frac{1}{2}$, $3\frac{1}{2}$
2. $1\frac{1}{3}$, $3\frac{2}{3}$	**7.** $2\frac{2}{5}$, $1\frac{4}{5}$
3. $1\frac{1}{2}$, $5\frac{1}{2}$	**8.** −$\frac{2}{5}$, $1\frac{3}{5}$
4. −$\frac{1}{2}$, $1\frac{1}{2}$	**9.** $2\frac{2}{5}$, $1\frac{1}{5}$
5. $\frac{1}{2}$, 2	**10.** $\frac{1}{3}$, $1\frac{2}{3}$

CHAPTER 8   Inverse and Square Matrices

Several topics in this chapter are not essential so selection may be necessary.

EXERCISE 8a   **1.** Yes, 3×3 **3.** Yes, 2×2 **5.** Yes, 2×2
                  2. No   **4.** No   **6.** Yes, 3×3

EXERCISE 8b   **1.** $\begin{pmatrix} 4 & 7 \\ 7 & 11 \end{pmatrix}$ **7.** $\begin{pmatrix} 11 & 7 \\ 7 & 4 \end{pmatrix}$

2. $(7 \;\; -6)$ **8.** Not possible

3. $\begin{pmatrix} 7 & 10 & 1 \\ 15 & 26 & 1 \end{pmatrix}$ **9.** $\begin{pmatrix} 4 & 24 & 4 \\ 3 & 18 & 3 \\ 2 & 12 & 2 \end{pmatrix}$

4. Not possible   **10.** (24)

5. Not possible   **11.** $\begin{pmatrix} 1 \\ -1 \end{pmatrix}$

6. $\begin{pmatrix} 26 & 13 \\ -4 & -2 \end{pmatrix}$ **12.** $(34 \;\; 6)$

EXERCISE 8c   **1.** $\begin{pmatrix} 4 & 2 \\ 3 & 4 \end{pmatrix}$ **4.** $\begin{pmatrix} 0 & 0 \\ 0 & 0 \end{pmatrix}$

2. $\begin{pmatrix} 4 \\ 5 \end{pmatrix}$ **5.** $(3 \;\; 2)$

3. $(0 \;\; 0)$ **6.** $\begin{pmatrix} 3 & 2 & -1 \\ 4 & 3 & 1 \end{pmatrix}$

EXERCISE 8d   **1.** $\begin{pmatrix} 1 & 0 \\ 0 & 1 \end{pmatrix}$ **5.** $\begin{pmatrix} 3 & 0 \\ 0 & 3 \end{pmatrix}$

2. $\begin{pmatrix} 5 & 0 \\ 0 & 5 \end{pmatrix}$ **6.** $\begin{pmatrix} 3 & 0 \\ 0 & 3 \end{pmatrix}$

3. $\begin{pmatrix} 5 & 0 \\ 0 & 5 \end{pmatrix}$ **7.** $\begin{pmatrix} -1 & 0 \\ 0 & -1 \end{pmatrix}$

4. $\begin{pmatrix} 2 & 0 \\ 0 & 2 \end{pmatrix}$ **8.** $\begin{pmatrix} 1 & 0 \\ 0 & 1 \end{pmatrix}$

10. $\begin{pmatrix} 6 & -2 \\ -8 & 3 \end{pmatrix}$ **13.** $\begin{pmatrix} 5 & 3 \\ -1 & 1 \end{pmatrix}$ **16.** $\begin{pmatrix} 8 & -4 \\ -9 & 5 \end{pmatrix}$

11. $\begin{pmatrix} 3 & -1 \\ -2 & 2 \end{pmatrix}$ **14.** $\begin{pmatrix} 4 & -7 \\ -3 & 5 \end{pmatrix}$ **17.** $\begin{pmatrix} 4 & -2 \\ -14 & 6 \end{pmatrix}$

12. $\begin{pmatrix} 3 & 1 \\ 20 & 6 \end{pmatrix}$ **15.** $\begin{pmatrix} 6 & -3 \\ -9 & 5 \end{pmatrix}$ **18.** $\begin{pmatrix} 1 & -2 \\ -2 & 1 \end{pmatrix}$

19. $\begin{pmatrix} -2 & 3 \\ -3 & 4 \end{pmatrix}$

EXERCISE 8e 1. $\begin{pmatrix} 2 & -1 \\ -7 & 4 \end{pmatrix}$ 3. $\begin{pmatrix} -2 & 3 \\ -7 & 10 \end{pmatrix}$ 5. $\begin{pmatrix} 7 & -4 \\ -12 & 7 \end{pmatrix}$

2. $\begin{pmatrix} 2 & -3 \\ -7 & 11 \end{pmatrix}$ 4. $\begin{pmatrix} 7 & -5 \\ -4 & 3 \end{pmatrix}$ 6. $\begin{pmatrix} 2 & -1 \\ -1 & 1 \end{pmatrix}$

EXERCISE 8f Before Number 16, ask the pupils to try to find the inverse of, say, $\begin{pmatrix} 2 & 1 \\ 4 & 2 \end{pmatrix}$ and discuss again the fact that division by zero is impossible—hence no inverse.

1. $\begin{pmatrix} 1\frac{1}{2} & -1 \\ -4 & 3 \end{pmatrix}$ 4. $\begin{pmatrix} \frac{1}{3} & \frac{2}{3} \\ -\frac{1}{3} & \frac{1}{3} \end{pmatrix}$ 7. $\begin{pmatrix} 4 & 3 \\ 5 & 4 \end{pmatrix}$

2. $\begin{pmatrix} \frac{1}{3} & -\frac{2}{3} \\ -1 & 3 \end{pmatrix}$ 5. $\begin{pmatrix} \frac{1}{2} & 0 \\ 0 & \frac{1}{3} \end{pmatrix}$ 8. $\begin{pmatrix} 4 & -3 \\ -5 & 4 \end{pmatrix}$

3. $\begin{pmatrix} 1\frac{1}{2} & -\frac{1}{2} \\ -2\frac{1}{2} & 1 \end{pmatrix}$ 6. $\begin{pmatrix} 4 & -1 \\ -5\frac{1}{2} & 1\frac{1}{2} \end{pmatrix}$ 9. $\begin{pmatrix} 1 & 1 \\ \frac{1}{2} & \frac{3}{4} \end{pmatrix}$

10. $\begin{pmatrix} -1 & 1 \\ 3\frac{1}{2} & -3 \end{pmatrix}$ 12. $\begin{pmatrix} -\frac{1}{5} & \frac{1}{5} \\ \frac{1}{5} & \frac{4}{5} \end{pmatrix}$ 14. $\begin{pmatrix} -1 & -1\frac{1}{3} \\ -1 & -1 \end{pmatrix}$

11. $\begin{pmatrix} -1 & 2 \\ 2\frac{1}{2} & -4\frac{1}{2} \end{pmatrix}$ 13. $\begin{pmatrix} -1 & 1 \\ 2 & -1\frac{1}{2} \end{pmatrix}$ 15. $\begin{pmatrix} -3 & 2 \\ 4 & -2\frac{1}{2} \end{pmatrix}$

16. a) Yes   b) No   c) Yes
17. a) Yes   b) Yes   c) Yes

18. $\begin{pmatrix} 1 & -1 \\ -1 & 1\frac{1}{5} \end{pmatrix}$ 20. $\begin{pmatrix} \frac{1}{5} & 0 \\ 0 & \frac{1}{5} \end{pmatrix}$ 22. $\begin{pmatrix} 2 & -1 \\ -3 & 1\frac{2}{3} \end{pmatrix}$

19. No inverse 21. $\begin{pmatrix} -4 & 7 \\ 3 & -5 \end{pmatrix}$ 23. No inverse

EXERCISE 8g 1. $1, \begin{pmatrix} 2 & -3 \\ -3 & 5 \end{pmatrix}$ 5. $\begin{pmatrix} 6 & -9\frac{1}{2} \\ -5 & 8 \end{pmatrix}$ 9. $\begin{pmatrix} 13 & -21 \\ -21 & 34 \end{pmatrix}$

2. $2, \begin{pmatrix} 1\frac{1}{2} & -1 \\ -1 & 1 \end{pmatrix}$ 6. $\begin{pmatrix} 6 & -5 \\ -9\frac{1}{2} & 8 \end{pmatrix}$ 10. $\begin{pmatrix} 13 & -21 \\ -21 & 34 \end{pmatrix}$

3. $\mathbf{I}$ 7. $\begin{pmatrix} 6 & -9\frac{1}{2} \\ -5 & 8 \end{pmatrix}$ 11. $\begin{pmatrix} 2 & 1 \\ -3\frac{1}{2} & -1\frac{1}{2} \end{pmatrix}$

4. $\begin{pmatrix} 16 & 19 \\ 10 & 12 \end{pmatrix}$ 8. $\begin{pmatrix} 34 & 21 \\ 21 & 13 \end{pmatrix}$ 12. $\begin{pmatrix} -2\frac{1}{2} & 4 \\ -2 & 3 \end{pmatrix}$

EXERCISE 8h The formula for finding the value of $|\mathbf{A}|$ is not essential and none of the questions in the rest of this chapter depends upon it.

1. 9   5. -14 9. 9
2. 17   6. 10   10. 5
3. 0   7. -1 11. 5
4. 19   8. -8 12. -9

EXERCISE 8i   Solution of simultaneous equations by elimination demands that decisions are made at several stages. Pupils may notice that using matrices to solve simultaneous equations is not as neat as the elimination method and generally takes longer. This is a good time to explain that, because no decisions have to be made when using matrices, it is an ideal method for computer programming.

1. $x + 2y = 3$
$3x + 2y = 5$

2. $4x + 2y = 12$
$5x + 3y = 15$

3. $9x + 2y = 24$
$4x + y = 11$

4. $6p - q = -8$
$2p + q = 0$

5. $\begin{pmatrix} 3 & 2 \\ 1 & 1 \end{pmatrix}\begin{pmatrix} x \\ y \end{pmatrix} = \begin{pmatrix} 8 \\ 3 \end{pmatrix}$

6. $\begin{pmatrix} 4 & -3 \\ 2 & 1 \end{pmatrix}\begin{pmatrix} x \\ y \end{pmatrix} = \begin{pmatrix} 1 \\ 3 \end{pmatrix}$

7. $\begin{pmatrix} 4 & 3 \\ 5 & 4 \end{pmatrix}\begin{pmatrix} x \\ y \end{pmatrix} = \begin{pmatrix} 5 \\ 6 \end{pmatrix}$

8. $\begin{pmatrix} 3 & -2 \\ 1 & -1 \end{pmatrix}\begin{pmatrix} x \\ y \end{pmatrix} = \begin{pmatrix} 1 \\ 0 \end{pmatrix}$

9. $\begin{pmatrix} 7 & -2 \\ 3 & 4 \end{pmatrix}\begin{pmatrix} x \\ y \end{pmatrix} = \begin{pmatrix} 3 \\ 11 \end{pmatrix}$

10. $\begin{pmatrix} 5 & 1 \\ 4 & -3 \end{pmatrix}\begin{pmatrix} x \\ y \end{pmatrix} = \begin{pmatrix} -8 \\ -14 \end{pmatrix}$

EXERCISE 8j

1. $x = 1,\ y = 2$
2. $x = 2,\ y = 3$
3. $x = 1,\ y = -1$
4. $x = 2,\ y = -1$
5. $a = 3,\ b = 0$

6. $x = 1,\ y = 2$
7. $x = 4,\ y = 2$
8. $x = 1,\ y = -2$
9. $x = 4,\ y = 2$
10. $p = 1,\ q = 1$
11. $s = -2,\ t = 3$

12. $\begin{pmatrix} 1 & 1 \\ 1 & 2 \end{pmatrix}\begin{pmatrix} x \\ y \end{pmatrix} = \begin{pmatrix} 2 \\ 3 \end{pmatrix}$; $x = 1,\ y = 1$

13. $\begin{pmatrix} 4 & -1 \\ 1 & 1 \end{pmatrix}\begin{pmatrix} x \\ y \end{pmatrix} = \begin{pmatrix} 5 \\ 5 \end{pmatrix}$; $x = 2,\ y = 3$

14. $\begin{pmatrix} 5 & 4 \\ 1 & 1 \end{pmatrix}\begin{pmatrix} x \\ y \end{pmatrix} = \begin{pmatrix} 1 \\ 0 \end{pmatrix}$; $x = 1,\ y = -1$

15. $\begin{pmatrix} 2 & 3 \\ 3 & 5 \end{pmatrix}\begin{pmatrix} x \\ y \end{pmatrix} = \begin{pmatrix} 15 \\ 23 \end{pmatrix}$; $x = 6,\ y = 1$

16. $\begin{pmatrix} 9 & 2 \\ 3 & 1 \end{pmatrix}\begin{pmatrix} x \\ y \end{pmatrix} = \begin{pmatrix} 11 \\ 5 \end{pmatrix}$; $x = \frac{1}{3},\ y = 4$

17. $\begin{pmatrix} 2 & 3 \\ 3 & 2 \end{pmatrix}\begin{pmatrix} x \\ y \end{pmatrix} = \begin{pmatrix} 7 \\ 8 \end{pmatrix}$; $x = 2,\ y = 1$

18. $\begin{pmatrix} 5 & 2 \\ 3 & -1 \end{pmatrix}\begin{pmatrix} x \\ y \end{pmatrix} = \begin{pmatrix} 16 \\ 3 \end{pmatrix}$; $x = 2,\ y = 3$

19. $\begin{pmatrix} 1 & 4 \\ 2 & 3 \end{pmatrix}\begin{pmatrix} x \\ y \end{pmatrix} = \begin{pmatrix} 11 \\ 7 \end{pmatrix}$; $x = -1,\ y = 3$

20. Determinant is zero so there is no inverse.
21. Determinant is zero so there is no inverse.

EXERCISE 8k **1.** $\begin{pmatrix} 5 & 6 \\ -3 & 0 \end{pmatrix}$

5. $\begin{pmatrix} 2 & 1\frac{1}{2} \\ 1 & \frac{1}{2} \end{pmatrix}$

2. $\begin{pmatrix} 7 & 2 \\ -3 & 2 \end{pmatrix}$

6. $\begin{pmatrix} 3 & -6 \\ 0 & 3 \end{pmatrix}$

3. $\begin{pmatrix} 15 & 19 \\ 9 & 9 \end{pmatrix}$

7. $\begin{pmatrix} 3 & -1 \\ -5 & 1 \end{pmatrix}$

4. $\begin{pmatrix} -5 & -6 \\ 3 & 0 \end{pmatrix}$

8. $\begin{pmatrix} -\frac{1}{2} & 1\frac{1}{2} \\ 1 & -2 \end{pmatrix}$

EXERCISE 8l **1.** $\begin{pmatrix} 5 & 4 & 3 \\ 10 & -8 & 4 \end{pmatrix}$

4. $\begin{pmatrix} \frac{4}{7} & -\frac{3}{7} \\ -\frac{3}{7} & \frac{4}{7} \end{pmatrix}$

2. $\begin{pmatrix} 1 & 3\frac{1}{2} \\ 1\frac{1}{2} & -\frac{1}{2} \end{pmatrix}$

5. (-9)

3. 24

6. $\begin{pmatrix} 13 & 33 \\ 6 & 22 \end{pmatrix}$

EXERCISE 8m **1.** $\begin{pmatrix} 5 & 3 \\ -1 & 4 \end{pmatrix}$

4. $\begin{pmatrix} 3 \\ -1 \end{pmatrix}$

2. 2

5. $(6 \ 10)$

3. $\begin{pmatrix} 1 & 1 \\ 2 & 3 \end{pmatrix}$

6. $(3 \ -1\frac{1}{2})$

Codes: The following is a fun way of using matrices and gives extra practice in the use of inverses. It does take a long time though, especially with those pupils who are careless!

We can use a 2×2 matrix to code a message and we can use its inverse for decoding. Choose a matrix with a determinant of 1 so that the entries in the inverse are whole numbers: for example $\begin{pmatrix} 2 & 1 \\ 1 & 1 \end{pmatrix}$ has as its inverse $\begin{pmatrix} 1 & -1 \\ -1 & 2 \end{pmatrix}$.

Give to each letter of the message a number according to its position in the alphabet.

G	O		A	W	A	Y
7	15		1	23	1	25

Make the number of letters up to a multiple of 4 by adding "A"s.

G	O		A	W	A	Y	A	A
7	15		1	23	1	25	1	1

Now we can form two 2×2 matrices from these numbers, i.e. $\begin{pmatrix} 7 & 15 \\ 1 & 23 \end{pmatrix}$ and $\begin{pmatrix} 1 & 25 \\ 1 & 1 \end{pmatrix}$.

Premultiply each by the coding matrix.

$$\begin{pmatrix} 2 & 1 \\ 1 & 1 \end{pmatrix}\begin{pmatrix} 7 & 15 \\ 1 & 23 \end{pmatrix} = \begin{pmatrix} 15 & 53 \\ 8 & 38 \end{pmatrix}$$

$$\begin{pmatrix} 2 & 1 \\ 1 & 1 \end{pmatrix}\begin{pmatrix} 1 & 25 \\ 1 & 1 \end{pmatrix} = \begin{pmatrix} 3 & 51 \\ 2 & 26 \end{pmatrix}$$

The coded message is 15, 53, 8, 38, 3, 51, 2, 26.

To decode the message we form matrices again from the coded message and use the decoder, that is, the inverse matrix. This gives the original numbers.

$$\begin{pmatrix} 1 & -1 \\ -1 & 2 \end{pmatrix}\begin{pmatrix} 15 & 53 \\ 8 & 38 \end{pmatrix} = \begin{pmatrix} 7 & 15 \\ 1 & 23 \end{pmatrix} \text{ and } \begin{pmatrix} 1 & -1 \\ -1 & 2 \end{pmatrix}\begin{pmatrix} 3 & 51 \\ 2 & 26 \end{pmatrix} = \begin{pmatrix} 1 & 25 \\ 1 & 1 \end{pmatrix}$$

The following messages have been coded using the given matrices.

1. GOODBYE $\qquad\qquad \begin{pmatrix} 2 & -1 \\ 3 & -1 \end{pmatrix}$ $-1, 26, 6, 41, -1, 49, 1, 74$

2. HAPPY BIRTHDAY $\begin{pmatrix} 3 & 4 \\ 2 & 3 \end{pmatrix}$ 88, 67, 64, 50, 111, 78, 77, 58, 76, 28, 52, 19, 79, 7, 53, 5

3. JACK AND JILL $\qquad \begin{pmatrix} 3 & 5 \\ 1 & 2 \end{pmatrix}$ 45, 58, 16, 23, 23, 92, 9, 34, 87, 41, 33, 14

4. GEOMETRY $\qquad\quad \begin{pmatrix} 4 & 7 \\ 1 & 2 \end{pmatrix}$ 133, 111, 37, 31, 146, 255, 41, 70

5 HULLO $\qquad\qquad\quad \begin{pmatrix} 2 & 1 \\ 1 & 1 \end{pmatrix}$ 28, 54, 20, 33, 31, 3, 16, 2

CHAPTER 9   Areas

EXERCISE 9a   Revises areas of rectangles, parallelograms and triangles.

1. $40\,\text{cm}^2$
2. $10\,\text{cm}^2$
3. $17\,\text{cm}^2$
4. $19.35\,\text{cm}^2$
5. 12 sq. units
6. 30 sq. units
7. 12 sq. units
8. 16 sq. units
9. $24\frac{1}{2}$ sq. units

10. 4 cm
11. $450\,\text{mm}^2$
12. 5 cm
13. 5 m, $25\,\text{m}^2$
14. 4 cm
15. a) $17.5\,\text{cm}^2$ b) 5.83 cm
16. a) $12\,\text{cm}^2$ b) 3.43 cm
17. a) $40\,\text{cm}^2$ b) 6.67 cm
18. a) $7\,\text{cm}^2$ b) 2 cm

EXERCISE 9b   Revises areas of compound shapes.

1. $60\,\text{cm}^2$
2. $40\,\text{cm}^2$
3. $30\,\text{cm}^2$
4. $45\,\text{cm}^2$
5. $135\,\text{cm}^2$
6. $27.75\,\text{cm}^2$

EXERCISE 9c   It is worth showing, by expanding $\frac{1}{2}(p+q) \times h$, that this is an alternative way of writing $\frac{1}{2}ph + \frac{1}{2}qh$, because "common factors" have not been covered at this stage.

1. $42\,\text{cm}^2$
2. $94.5\,\text{cm}^2$
3. $21\,\text{cm}^2$
4. $8.75\,\text{cm}^2$

5. 30 sq. units
6. 33 sq. units
7. 56 sq. units

8. 16 sq. units
9. 84 sq. units
10. 47 sq. units

EXERCISE 9d   This and the next exercise can be omitted, or used for discussion only.

1. Area of each parallelogram is 35 cm²
2. Area of each triangle is 28 cm²
3. Each parallelogram has a base of length 4 units and height of 3 units. The areas are each equal to 12 sq. units
4. Each base is 6 units long. Each height is 3 units. The areas are each equal to 9 sq. units
8. Ratio of heights is 4 : 5 : 7 : 9. Ratio of areas is 4 : 5 : 7 : 9.
The ratio of areas is equal to the ratio of heights
9. The *y* coordinate of D is 9 (or −7 if drawn below the *x*-axis)
10. The *y* coordinate of E is 3 (or −1 if drawn below the *x*-axis)

EXERCISE 9e   Use for discussion with everyone. Only the most able should attempt these on their own. It is particularly difficult to produce a *reasoned* answer for Number 11. For Numbers 12 and 13 pupils need to be reminded how to construct parallel lines.

7. 12 cm   **8.** 2 : 1   **9.** 14 cm   **10.** 8 cm   **11.** 30°
12. △BEC = 27 cm², △DEC = 12 cm²   **13.** 132°   **14.** 6 cm

CHAPTER 10   Angles in Circles

Many pupils have problems with circle questions because they do not have a clear understanding of a) the meaning of "subtends", b) what a segment of a circle is. The first two exercises attempt to remedy this.

EXERCISE 10a   1. AB, AC, AD, BC, BD, CD. Yes, AC.

2.

4.

3.

5.

EXERCISE 10b
1. Minor arc DC
2. Minor arc BC
3. AĈB, AD̂B
4. BÂC, BD̂C
5. DA
6. AB
7. Minor arc BE
8. Minor arc CD
9. CE
10. DB

11. a) AĈB, AÊB   b) BÂC, BÊC
12. a) AB̂E, AĈE, AD̂E   b) CD̂E, CÂE, CB̂E

Experimental Work   Some teachers (and pupils!) may find the experimental work detailed below quite useful. The work may be illustrated by the teacher or, better still, pupils should be encouraged to make their own models using, for example, covers from old exercise books.

As an introduction you may choose to go through all the experiments (results) at one sitting, but to repeat them as each new fact is taught. Four experiments are listed, three of them yielding the five facts used in this chapter. The alternate segment result will not be used until Book 4A, but it is certainly worth a mention here since the model illustrates it so nicely.

All the results can be confirmed by diagrams and measurements.

Preparing the Model   You require two pieces of cardboard or stiff paper, preferably of different colours. The first should be a square of side approximately 18 cm and the other a rectangle measuring 20 cm by 12 cm.

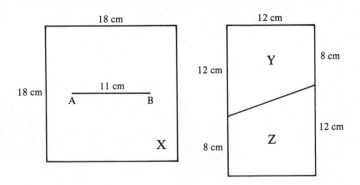

In the square piece cut a slot AB, 11 cm long, near the middle of the card. Cut the second piece along the line shown in the diagram to give two identical trapeziums Y and Z.

Experiment 1: (illustrating "angles in the same segment" and "opposite angles of a cyclic quadrilateral" result.)

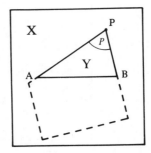

Take the trapezium Y and mark the acute angle P. Push P through the slot AB from behind, until the trapezium will not go any further. Mark with a dot the position of P on the square X.

Rotate the card Y into another position (again making sure that Y fills the slot) and mark the new position of P. Do this several times marking each position of P as shown below.

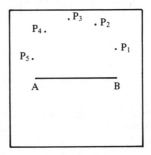

Now mark the obtuse angle of Y with the letter Q.

Push Y through the slot from behind as shown in the diagram and mark the position of Q. Rotate Y to give several positions of Q.

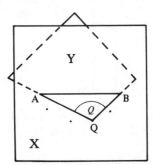

Take Y out and note that all the marked points look as though they lie on a circle. The different positions of P seem to lie on a major arc and the different positions of Q on a minor arc.

Card X should now look like this:

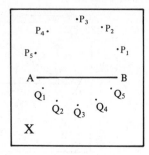

Experiment 2:   (illustrating "angle at centre" result).

Take Y and Z and place them together as shown below (you might find it useful to sellotape them together).

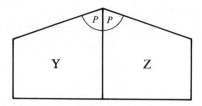

Now push them together through the slot AB from behind, keeping the edges of Y and Z parallel to the edges of the rectangle as indicated. Mark O as shown.

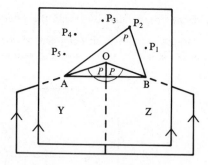

Take Y and Z out of the slot. With centre O and radius OA draw the major arc AB which will be seen to pass through P_1, P_2,....

Experiment 3:   (illustrating "angle in a semicircle" result).

Turn the square card over to use the opposite side. Use one of the right angles from Y or Z and place it upwards through the slot AB from behind. Mark the position of the right angle R. Repeat this with R in several different positions.

Now place the right angle downwards through AB from behind and mark several additional positions of R.

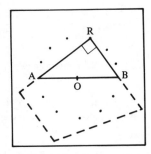

Remove the trapezium and find the midpoint O of AB. Centre O, radius OA, draw a circle.

Experiment 4:　("alternate segment" result).

Fig. 1.

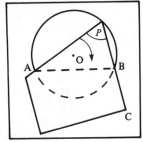

Fig. 2.

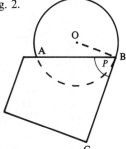

Place one trapezium on the circle obtained in the first experiment such that it gives one position for P. This is shown in Figure 1. Now rotate the trapezium downwards about A so that P moves along the circle towards B. Figure 2 shows the position when AP coincides with AB. OB is a radius and you can see that the side CB on the trapezium has only one point of contact with the circle, that is at B.

CB is a tangent to the circle at B

Since $A\hat{P}B = A\hat{B}C$ this experiment shows that:

> the angle between a tangent and a chord drawn at the point of contact, is equal to the angle in the alternate segment.

EXERCISE 10c Answers depend on pupils' drawings but in each question the angles should be equal.

EXERCISE 10d
1. $h = 38°$
2. $i = 39°, j = 46°$
3. $x = 33° = y$
4. $p = 72°, q = 57°$
5. $l = 100°$
6. $x = 108°, y = 26°$
7. $w = 57°, x = 123°$
8. $c = 144°$

EXERCISE 10e Answers depend on pupils' drawings but in each question $y = 2x$.

EXERCISE 10f **1.** $d = 80°$ **3.** $f = 114°$ **5.** $g = 98°$ **7.** $l = 132°$
                           2. $e = 64°$ **4.** $i = 38°$ **6.** $h = 32°$ **8.** $m = 102°$

EXERCISE 10g Answers depend on pupils' drawings but in each question $p + q = 180°$.

EXERCISE 10h **1.** $d = 108°$ **3.** $f = 103°$ **5.** $l = 131°$ **7.** $g = 121°, h = 68°$
                            2. $e = 84°$ **4.** $k = 115°$ **6.** $m = 87°, n = 112°$ **8.** $i = 110°, j = 50°$

EXERCISE 10i Answers depend on pupils' drawings but the conclusions should be:

   1. $p = q$ **3.** $s = r$ **5.** $y = 100°$ **7.** $p = 54°, q = 76°$
   2. $v = u$ **4.** $x = w$ **6.** $z = 109°$ **8.** $r = 126°, s = 83°$

EXERCISE 10j **1.** $d = 75°, e = 65°, f = 140°$
                            2. $p = 60°, q = 60°, r = 120°, s = 60°$
                            3. $k = 30°, l = 30°, m = 30°, n = 60°$
                            4. $g = 24°, h = 156°, i = 74°$
                            5. $w = 73°, x = 34°, y = 34°, z = 73°$
                            6. $d = 64°, e = 64°, f = 116°, g = 116°, b = 64°$
                            7. $a = 44°$ **8.** $c = 60°, d = 46°$
                            9. $g = 116°$ **10.** $b = 78°$
                           11. $e = 34°, f = 52°$ **12.** $h = 72°$
                           13. $l = 154°, m = 40°, n = 37°$
                           14. $r = 110°, s = 122°$
                           15. $x = 30°, y = 58°, z = 88°$
                           16. $c = 25°, d = 25°, e = 50°$
                           17. $h = 116°, i = 32°$
                           18. $l = 126°, m = 63°, n = 117°$
                           19. $u = 34°, v = 68°, w = 56°, x = 56°$
                           20. $k = 62°, l = 56°, m = 124°, n = 16°$

EXERCISE 10k **1.** $d = 90° = e$ **2.** $f = 90° = g$ **3.** $h = 90° = i$

EXERCISE 10l **1.** $d = 90°, e = 53°$ **4.** $l = 90°, m = 61°$
                            2. $f = 90°, g = 45°$ **5.** $j = 90°, k = 55°$
                            3. $h = 90°, i = 26°$ **6.** $p = 90°, q = 38°$

                            7. $r = 90°, s = 52°, t = 90°, u = 43°$
                            8. $d = 90°, e = 45°, f = 90°, g = 18°$
                            9. $c = 90°, d = 58°, e = 32°$
                           10. $v = 90°, w = 47°, x = 90°, y = 51°$
                           11. $j = 90°, k = 33°, l = 33°, m = 57°$
                           12. $f = 45°, g = 58°, h = 45°, i = 32°$

EXERCISE 10m **1.** $d = 106°$ **3.** $d = 34°,\ e = 68°$
　　　　　　　 2. $e = f = 38°$ **4.** $x = 75°,\ y = 15°,\ z = 132°$

　　　　　　　 5. $p = 36° = q,\ r = 39°$
　　　　　　　 6. $x = 112°,\ y = 68°,\ z = 112°$
　　　　　　　 7. $g = 54°,\ h = 120°$
　　　　　　　 8. $d = 37°,\ e = 53°,\ f = 57°,\ g = 33°$

CHAPTER 11   Algebraic Products

Much of the work in this chapter can be done as oral classwork.

EXERCISE 11a **1.** $2x + 2$ **4.** $5a + 20$ **7.** $5 - 5b$
　　　　　　　 2. $3x - 3$ **5.** $3b + 21$ **8.** $6a - 2$
　　　　　　　 3. $4x + 12$ **6.** $3 - 3a$ **9.** $8 + 12b$

　　　　　　 10. $5ab - 5ac$ **13.** $15xy + 5xz$ **16.** $16rt - 8rs$
　　　　　　 11. $4ab - 8ac$ **14.** $16xy + 12yz$ **17.** $3ab - 15ac$
　　　　　　 12. $6a^2 + 3ab$ **15.** $6np - 10nq$ **18.** $12xy + 8xz$

EXERCISE 11b The suggested order for multiplying the terms in the two brackets gives lines which some pupils see as forming a face. Two lines give the eyebrows, while the other two form the nose and chin.
Some teachers may prefer a different order, e.g.

$$(\overbrace{a + b})(c + d) = ac + ad + bc + bd$$

　　　　　 1. $ac + ad + bc + bd$ **6.** $ac + ad - bc - bd$
　　　　　 2. $ps + pt + qs + qt$ **7.** $xy + xz + y^2 + yz$
　　　　　 3. $2ac + 4ad + bc + 2bd$ **8.** $6ac + 2ad + 3bc + bd$
　　　　　 4. $5xz + 15x + 2yz + 6y$ **9.** $5xz + 10x + 4yz + 8y$
　　　　　 5. $xz - 4x + yz - 4y$ **10.** $15x - 3xz - 10y + 2yz$

　　　　 11. $2ps - 3pt + 2qs - 3qt$ **16.** $12pr - 9ps - 4qr + 3qs$
　　　　 12. $ac - ad - 2bc + 2bd$ **17.** $9ac + 12ad - 12bc - 16bd$
　　　　 13. $6uw - 30ur - 5vw + 25vr$ **18.** $21x - 14xz - 6y + 4yz$
　　　　 14. $6ac - 9ad + 8bc - 12bd$ **19.** $10ac - 4a + 5bc - 2b$
　　　　 15. $9xz + 6x + 6yz + 4y$ **20.** $15a - 10ad - 12b + 8bd$

EXERCISE 11c With other than above average pupils it is probably wise to write down the four terms obtained by multiplying the brackets, and then to collect like terms as a separate step.

　　　　　 1. $x^2 + 7x + 12$ **3.** $x^2 + 7x + 6$
　　　　　 2. $x^2 + 6x + 8$ **4.** $x^2 + 7x + 10$

5. $x^2 + 11x + 24$

6. $a^2 + 9a + 20$

7. $b^2 + 9b + 14$

8. $c^2 + 10c + 24$

9. $p^2 + 15p + 36$

10. $q^2 + 17q + 70$

11. $x^2 - 5x + 6$

12. $x^2 - 12x + 35$

13. $a^2 - 10a + 16$

14. $x^2 - 13x + 30$

15. $b^2 - 10b + 25$

16. $x^2 - 7x + 12$

17. $x^2 - 12x + 32$

18. $b^2 - 6b + 8$

19. $a^2 - 8a + 16$

20. $p^2 - 15p + 56$

21. $x^2 + x - 6$

22. $x^2 + x - 20$

23. $x^2 - 3x - 28$

24. $a^2 - 7a - 30$

25. $p^2 - 25$

26. $x^2 + 5x - 14$

27. $x^2 + x - 30$

28. $x^2 + 9x - 10$

29. $b^2 - 15b + 56$

30. $z^2 - 13z + 12$

EXERCISE 11d The value of setting out as given in the text will become apparent when factorising is considered in the next chapter.

1. $x^2 + 9x + 20$

2. $a^2 + 7a + 10$

3. $x^2 - 9x + 20$

4. $a^2 - 7a + 10$

5. $x^2 + 14x + 48$

6. $a^2 + 17a + 70$

7. $x^2 - 14x + 48$

8. $a^2 - 17a + 70$

9. $a^2 - 3a - 10$

10. $y^2 - 3y - 18$

11. $z^2 - 6z - 40$

12. $p^2 - 3p - 40$

13. $a^2 - 3a - 70$

14. $y^2 + 8y - 20$

15. $z^2 - 11z - 12$

16. $p^2 - 11p - 26$

17. $x^2 - 6x + 5$

18. $b^2 + 16b + 63$

19. $a^2 - 16$

20. $r^2 - 12r - 28$

21. $p^2 + 14p + 24$

22. $t^2 - 7t - 60$

23. $c^2 + 3c - 40$

24. $x^2 - 25$

EXERCISE 11e

1. $2x^2 + 3x + 1$

2. $5x^2 + 12x + 4$

3. $5x^2 + 17x + 6$

4. $3x^2 + 19x + 20$

5. $3x^2 + 5x + 2$

6. $3x^2 + 11x + 6$

7. $4x^2 + 7x + 3$

8. $7x^2 + 23x + 6$

9. $6x^2 + 13x + 6$

10. $12x^2 - 25x + 12$

11. $10x^2 - 3x - 18$

12. $21a^2 - 58a + 21$

13. $10x^2 + 31x + 15$

14. $21x^2 - 20x + 4$

15. $12x^2 - 5x - 2$

16. $6b^2 - 5b - 25$

17. $4a^2 - 9$

18. $9b^2 - 49$

19. $49y^2 - 25$

20. $20a^2 + a - 12$

21. $16x^2 - 9$

22. $25y^2 - 4$

23. $9x^2 - 1$

24. $16x^2 - 8x - 35$

25. $6x^2 + 5x + 1$

26. $-5x^2 + 8x + 4$

27. $-6x^2 + 19x - 3$

28. $-35a^2 + 29a - 6$

29. $8 + 10x - 3x^2$

30. $4x^2 + 7x - 15$

31. $15x^2 + 26x + 8$

32. $-14x^2 + 13x + 12$

33. $-20x^2 + 27x - 9$

34. $12 - p - p^2$

35. $x^2 - 3x - 10$

36. $4x^2 + 9x - 9$

Better pupils would be expected to remember and use the screened results. Some teachers may like to illustrate these results geometrically, for example:

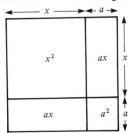

Area of whole $= (x + a)^2$

Total area of separate parts $= x^2 + ax + ax + a^2$

$\qquad\qquad\qquad\qquad\quad = x^2 + 2ax + x^2$

Therefore $\qquad (x + a)^2 = x^2 + 2ax + a^2$

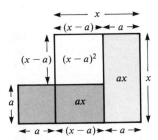

Area of whole $=$ area of large square $+$ area of small square

$\qquad\qquad\qquad = x^2 + a^2$

Area of whole also $= (x - a)^2 + ax + ax$

Therefore $\qquad\qquad\qquad (x - a)^2 + 2ax = x^2 + a^2$

i.e. $\qquad\qquad\qquad\qquad (x - a)^2 = x^2 - 2ax + a^2$

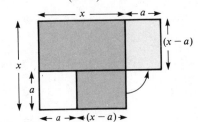

Area shaded is $x^2 - a^2$

The rectangle measuring $(x + a)$ by $(x - a)$ has an equal area which is $(x + a)(x - a)$

Therefore $\qquad\qquad\qquad x^2 - a^2 = (x + a)(x - a)$

EXERCISE 11f
1. $x^2 + 2x + 1$
2. $x^2 + 4x + 4$
3. $a^2 + 6a + 9$
4. $b^2 + 8b + 16$

5. $t^2 + 20t + 100$
6. $x^2 + 24x + 144$
7. $x^2 + 16x + 64$
8. $p^2 + 14p + 49$

9. $x^2 + 2xy + y^2$
10. $y^2 + 2yz + z^2$
11. $c^2 + 2cd + d^2$
12. $m^2 + 2mn + n^2$

13. $p^2 + 2pq + q^2$
14. $a^2 + 2ab + b^2$
15. $e^2 + 2ef + f^2$
16. $u^2 + 2uv + v^2$

17. $4x^2 + 4x + 1$
18. $16b^2 + 8b + 1$
19. $25x^2 + 20x + 4$
20. $36c^2 + 12c + 1$

21. $9a^2 + 6a + 1$
22. $4x^2 + 20x + 25$
23. $9a^2 + 24a + 16$
24. $16y^2 + 24y + 9$

25. $x^2 + 4xy + 4y^2$
26. $9x^2 + 6xy + y^2$
27. $4x^2 + 20xy + 25y^2$
28. $9a^2 + 12ab + 4b^2$

29. $9a^2 + 6ab + b^2$
30. $p^2 + 8pq + 16q^2$
31. $49x^2 + 28xy + 4y^2$
32. $9s^2 + 24st + 16t^2$

33. $x^2 - 4x + 4$
34. $x^2 - 12x + 36$
35. $a^2 - 20a + 100$
36. $x^2 - 2xy + y^2$

37. $x^2 - 6x + 9$
38. $x^2 - 14x + 49$
39. $a^2 - 2ab + b^2$
40. $u^2 - 2uv + v^2$

41. $9x^2 - 6x + 1$
42. $25z^2 - 10z + 1$
43. $100a^2 - 180a + 81$
44. $16x^2 - 24x + 9$

45. $4a^2 - 4a + 1$
46. $16y^2 - 8y + 1$
47. $49b^2 - 28b + 4$
48. $25x^2 - 30x + 9$

49. $4y^2 - 4yx + x^2$
50. $25x^2 - 10xy + y^2$
51. $9m^2 - 12mn + 4n^2$
52. $49x^2 - 42xy + 9y^2$

53. $a^2 - 6ab + 9b^2$
54. $m^2 - 16mn + 64n^2$
55. $25a^2 - 20ab + 4b^2$
56. $9p^2 - 30pq + 25q^2$

EXERCISE 11g
1. $x^2 - 16$
2. $b^2 - 36$
3. $c^2 - 9$
4. $x^2 - 144$

5. $x^2 - 25$
6. $a^2 - 49$
7. $q^2 - 100$
8. $x^2 - 64$

9. $4x^2 - 1$
10. $9x^2 - 1$
11. $49a^2 - 4$
12. $25a^2 - 16$

13. $25x^2 - 1$
14. $4a^2 - 9$
15. $100m^2 - 1$
16. $36a^2 - 25$

17. $9x^2 - 16y^2$
18. $4a^2 - 25b^2$
19. $1 - 4a^2$
20. $49y^2 - 9z^2$
21. $100a^2 - 81b^2$

22. $25a^2 - 16b^2$
23. $1 - 9x^2$
24. $9 - 25x^2$
25. $25m^2 - 64n^2$
26. $36p^2 - 49q^2$

EXERCISE 11h
1. $2x^2 + 9x + 12$
2. $2x^2 + 9x + 2$
3. $x^2 + 15x + 32$
4. $a^2 - 9a + 36$
5. $2a^2 - 10a - 3$

6. $x^2 + 13x + 25$
7. $x^2 - 2x - 21$
8. $x^2 - 2x - 23$
9. $16x^2 + 6x - 10$
10. $12x^2 + 8x - 20$

11. $x^2y^2 - 6xy + 9$
12. $25 - 10yz + y^2z^2$
13. $x^2y^2 + 8xy + 16$
14. $9p^2q^2 + 48pq + 64$
15. $a^2 - 2abc + b^2c^2$

16. $a^2b^2 - 4ab + 4$
17. $36 - 12pq + p^2q^2$
18. $m^2n^2 + 6mn + 9$
19. $u^2v^2 - 4uvw + 4w^2$

Summary: This could prove very useful for periodic revision using home grown examples or the mixed exercises that follow.

EXERCISE 11i
1. $5x + 10$
2. $24pq - 16pr$
3. $6a^2 - 13ab - 5b^2$
4. $12x^2 - 17x - 5$
5. $x^2 + 16x + 60$

6. $x^2 - 20x + 96$
7. $16y^2 - 16y - 21$
8. $16y^2 - 81$
9. $25x^2 + 20x + 4$
10. $4a^2 - 28ab + 49b^2$

EXERCISE 11j
1. $8 - 20x$
2. $16a - 24a^2$
3. $12a^2 - 35a - 33$
4. $x^2 + 2x - 99$
5. $-20x^2 - 48x + 5$

6. $y^2 + 4yz + 4z^2$
7. $36y^2 + 24yz - 5z^2$
8. $16a^2 + 8a + 1$
9. $25a^2 - 70a + 49$
10. $36z^2 - 156zy + 169y^2$

EXERCISE 11k
1. $6 - 3a$
2. $8ab + 4ac$
3. $10ac + 25ad + 4bc + 10bd$
4. $x^2 - 19x + 84$
5. $a^2 + 16a + 63$

6. $a^2 - a - 20$
7. $6x^2 + 11x + 3$
8. $25x^2 - 4$
9. $9x^2 - 42x + 49$
10. $25x^2 - 4y^2$

EXERCISE 11l
1. $15 - 5x$
2. $36x^2 - 24x$
3. $6xy - 15xz$
4. $ac + ad - bc - bd$
5. $x^2 + 3x - 28$

6. $x^2 - 11x + 18$
7. $12x^2 + 11x + 2$
8. $x^2 - 8xy + 16y^2$
9. $4x^2 + 28xz + 49z^2$
10. $1 - 25a^2$

CHAPTER 12 Algebraic Factors

Each type of factor could be introduced as the converse of an expansion from the previous chapter.

EXERCISE 12a We start with common factors which are often forgotten when factorising at a later date. Encourage multiplying out to check the results.

1. $4(x+1)$ **4.** $5(a-2b)$ **7.** $4(3a+1)$
2. $3(4x-1)$ **5.** $3(t-3)$ **8.** $2(a+2b)$
3. $2(3a+1)$ **6.** $5(2a-1)$ **9.** $7(2x-1)$

10. $x(x+2)$ **13.** $x(2x+1)$ **16.** $x(x-4)$
11. $x(x-7)$ **14.** $2t(2-t)$ **17.** $b(b+4)$
12. $a(a+6)$ **15.** $x(x+5)$ **18.** $a(4a-1)$

19. $2x(x-3)$ **22.** $4x(3x+4)$ **25.** $2a(a-6)$
20. $2z(z^2+2)$ **23.** $5b(a-2c)$ **26.** $2p(3p+1)$
21. $5a(5a-1)$ **24.** $3y(y+9)$ **27.** $3y(3y-2)$

28. $2(x^2+2x+3)$ **33.** $3(x^2-2x+3)$
29. $5(2a^2-a+4)$ **34.** $4(a^2+2a-1)$
30. $b(a+4c-3d)$ **35.** $x(5y+4z+3)$
31. $4(2x-y+3z)$ **36.** $5b(a+2c+d)$
32. $3a(3b-2c-d)$ **37.** $2y(x-2z+4w)$

38. $x^2(x+1)$ **43.** $a^2(1+a)$
39. $x^2(1-x)$ **44.** $b^2(b-1)$
40. $5a^2(4-a)$ **45.** $2x^2(2x-1)$
41. $4x^2(3x-4)$ **46.** $9a^2(3-2a)$
42. $4x^2(x^2+3)$ **47.** $5x^2(2-3x^2)$

48. $4(3x+2)$ **53.** $x(x-8)$
49. $4x(2x+3)$ **54.** $3(4+3y^2)$
50. $3(3x^2-2x+4)$ **55.** $4x(3y+4z+2)$
51. $5x(x^2-2)$ **56.** $2x(2x^2+3)$
52. $4q(2p+r)$ **57.** $4bc(3a-2d)$

58. $\frac{1}{2}h(a+b)$ **64.** $2g(h_1-h_2)$
59. $m(g-a)$ **65.** $m(\frac{1}{2}v^2-gh)$

60. $\frac{1}{2}m(v^2+u^2)$ **66.** $\dfrac{\pi r^2}{3}(4r-h)$

61. $p\left(1+\dfrac{RT}{100}\right)$ **67.** $\pi r(3r+2h)$

62. $\pi r(2r+h)$ **68.** $\frac{1}{2}mu(u+1)$
63. $\pi(R^2+r^2)$ **69.** $\frac{1}{4}c(2b-a)$

EXERCISE 12b While it is possible to pair terms with common factors in more than one way, the pupil will soon discover that some pairings don't give common factors.

1. $(x+3)(y+3)$ **5.** $(x+1)(y+z)$
2. $(a+2b)(1+b)$ **6.** $(x+2)(y+4)$
3. $(a+b)(a+c)$ **7.** $(a+b)(c+4)$
4. $(x-3)(y+2)$ **8.** $(x+4)(y-2)$

9. $(p+q)(r+s)$

10. $(y+4)(x-3)$

11. $(x+2)(y-5)$

12. $(p+q)(r-s)$

13. $(a+2)(b-3)$

14. $(p-q)(r+s)$

15. $(p+4)(q+2)$

16. $(2+a)(3+b)$

17. $(p-q)(r-s)$

18. $(3a-b)(3-b)$

19. $(2a-b)(1-b)$

20. $(a-2)(a+2b)$

21. $(2-x)(3-y)$

22. $(a-2)(4a-b)$

23. $(3a-b)(2a-3)$

24. $(2m-3n)(1-n)$

25. $(t+r)(t+s)$

26. $(x-1)(x+y)$

27. $2(1-a)(2a+b)$

28. $(x+y)(1-y)$

29. $(2a+3b)(2-3a)$

30. $(a+b)(2a+c)$

31. $2(2x+y)(1-y)$

32. $(x+y)(y+z)$

33. $(x-2)(5-y)$

34. $(a+4)(b-3)$

35. $(x+3)(y-z)$

36. $(p-4)(2-q)$

37. $(a-2)(b-3)$

38. $(a-4)(3-b)$

39. $(m+n)(m+1)$

40. $(a+1)(a-b)$

41. $(2p+1)(p-2q)$

42. $(x+1)(1-y)$

43. $(a+b)(a+1)$

44. $(a-b)(a+1)$

45. $(x+y)(x-1)$

46. $(a-1)(2a+b)$

47. $(x+2y)(5x-1)$

48. $(n-1)(m-1)$

49. $(x-1)(3x+y)$

50. $(2p-1)(p+2q)$

51. $(1-a)(3a+b)$

52. $(1-z)(2x+y)$

EXERCISE 12c It is important to point out that it does not matter which bracket is written first, i.e. $(x+2)(x+3)$ is identical to $(x+3)(x+2)$.

1. $(x+1)(x+2)$

2. $(x+1)(x+5)$

3. $(x+3)(x+4)$

4. $(x+3)(x+5)$

5. $(x+1)(x+20)$

6. $(x+1)(x+7)$

7. $(x+6)(x+2)$

8. $(x+1)(x+12)$

9. $(x+1)(x+15)$

10. $(x+2)(x+10)$

11. $(x+4)(x+4)$

12. $(x+3)(x+12)$

13. $(x+1)(x+18)$

14. $(x+2)(x+20)$

15. $(x+1)(x+8)$

16. $(x+3)(x+3)$

17. $(x+2)(x+18)$

18. $(x+3)(x+6)$

19. $(x+5)(x+6)$

20. $(x+4)(x+10)$

EXERCISE 12d

1. $(x-1)(x-8)$

2. $(x-3)(x-4)$

3. $(x-2)(x-15)$

4. $(x-4)(x-7)$

5. $(x-6)(x-7)$

6. $(x-2)(x-3)$

7. $(x-1)(x-15)$

8. $(x-3)(x-3)$

9. $(x-2)(x-16)$

10. $(x-7)(x-9)$

EXERCISE 12e
1. $(x+2)(x-3)$
2. $(x+5)(x-4)$
3. $(x-4)(x+3)$
4. $(x-4)(x+7)$
5. $(x+5)(x-3)$
6. $(x-6)(x+4)$
7. $(x-3)(x+9)$
8. $(x-11)(x+2)$
9. $(x-7)(x+5)$
10. $(x-10)(x+2)$

EXERCISE 12f To some, the worked example may appear to be too detailed. Most pupils require a definite plan of attack and will find the given method very helpful until they feel confident enough to go straight to the answer.

1. $(x+2)(x+7)$
2. $(x-3)(x-7)$
3. $(x+7)(x-2)$
4. $(x+6)(x-5)$
5. $(x+1)(x+8)$
6. $(x-5)(x-5)$
7. $(x+9)(x-1)$
8. $(x-13)(x-2)$

9. $(x+8)(x-7)$
10. $(x+2)(x+30)$
11. $(x+3)(x-9)$
12. $(x+20)(x-4)$
13. $(x+1)(x+13)$
14. $(x-2)(x+14)$
15. $(x+10)(x-8)$
16. $(x-5)(x-6)$

17. $(x-4)(x+12)$
18. $(x+6)(x+12)$
19. $(x+4)(x+13)$
20. $(x+2)(x-14)$
21. $(x+3)(x+8)$
22. $(x+3)(x-14)$
23. $(x-2)(x-16)$
24. $(x+12)(x-5)$

EXERCISE 12g
1. $(x+1)(x+8)$
2. $(x-3)(x-3)$
3. $(x+4)(x+7)$
4. $(4-x)(5+x)$
5. $(x+3)(x+3)$
6. $(x-1)(x-8)$
7. $(x+2)(x+15)$
8. $(9+x)(3-x)$

9. $(x+2)(x+11)$
10. $(x-13)(x+2)$
11. $(x-1)(x-7)$
12. $(x-6)(x+7)$
13. $(x-8)(x+3)$
14. $(x-2)(x-7)$
15. $(x+1)(x+27)$
16. $(x-7)(x+9)$

17. $(x+5)^2$
18. $(x-5)^2$
19. $(x+2)^2$
20. $(x-7)^2$
21. $(x+6)^2$
22. $(x-6)^2$
23. $(x-2)^2$
24. $(x+8)^2$

EXERCISE 12h Many pupils need much convincing that $6-5x-x^2$ and x^2+5x-6 do not factorise to give the same answers. The problem is not helped later when $6-5x-x^2 = 0$ becomes $x^2+5x-6 = 0$. Time spent on distinguishing between an expression and an equation, i.e. on the difference between factorising an expression and using factors to solve an equation, will be time well spent.

1. $(2+x)(1-x)$
2. $(3-x)(2+x)$
3. $(1-x)(4+x)$
4. $(4-x)(2+x)$

5. $(3+x)(2-x)$
6. $(2-x)(1+x)$

7. $(4+x)(2-x)$
8. $(5+x)(1-x)$

9. $(5+x)(2-x)$
10. $(6-x)(2+x)$
11. $(5-x)(1+x)$
12. $(7+x)(2-x)$

13. $(6-x)(1+x)$
14. $(5+x)(4-x)$
15. $(5+x)(3-x)$
16. $(4-x)(3+x)$

EXERCISE 12i

1. $(x+5)(x-5)$
2. $(x+2)(x-2)$
3. $(x+10)(x-10)$

4. $(x+1)(x-1)$
5. $(x+8)(x-8)$
6. $(x+4)(x-4)$

7. $(x+6)(x-6)$
8. $(x+9)(x-9)$
9. $(x+7)(x-7)$

10. $(3+x)(3-x)$
11. $(6+x)(6-x)$
12. $(10+x)(10-x)$

13. $(a+b)(a-b)$
14. $(3y+z)(3y-z)$
15. $(4+x)(4-x)$

16. $(5+x)(5-x)$
17. $(9+x)(9-x)$
18. $(x+y)(x-y)$

EXERCISE 12j

1. $3(x+4)$
2. $5x(5x+2)$
3. $4(3x^2-2)$
4. $7(2x+3)$
5. $2(2x^2+1)$

6. $7(3x-1)$
7. $9x(x-2)$
8. $4(5x+3)$
9. $2(2x-7)$
10. $4x(2x-1)$

11. $2(x+3)(x+4)$
12. $3(x-1)(x-8)$
13. $7(x+1)^2$
14. $4(x+3)(x-4)$
15. $5(x+1)(x+7)$

16. $3(x+2)(x+6)$
17. $4(x-3)^2$
18. $5(x+2)(x-3)$
19. $2(x+2)(x-11)$
20. $3(x-5)(x+8)$

EXERCISE 12k

1. $(2x+1)(x+1)$
2. $(3x-2)(x-1)$
3. $(4x+3)(x+1)$
4. $(2x-1)(x-3)$
5. $(3x+1)(x+4)$

6. $(3x-2)(x-2)$
7. $(2x+1)(x+4)$
8. $(5x-2)(x-3)$
9. $(2x+3)(x+4)$
10. $(7x-1)(x-4)$

11. $(2x+1)(x-2)$
12. $(3x+4)(x-1)$
13. $(5x+2)(x-3)$
14. $(x+2)(4x-3)$
15. $(3x-2)(x+4)$

16. $(7x+2)(x-3)$
17. $(6x+5)(x-2)$
18. $(5x-4)(x-3)$
19. $(3x+4)(x-5)$
20. $(4x-3)(x+5)$

EXERCISE 12l

1. $(3x+2)(2x+1)$
2. $(2x+3)(3x+5)$
3. $(3x+1)(5x+2)$
4. $(2x+3)(6x+5)$
5. $(7x+2)(5x+2)$

6. $(3x-1)(2x-3)$
7. $(3x-2)(3x-4)$
8. $(2x-1)(8x-1)$
9. $(5x-3)(3x-7)$
10. $(5x-2)(4x-3)$

11. $(4x+1)(2x-3)$
12. $(5x-2)(3x+1)$
13. $(3x+2)(7x-4)$
14. $(10x+3)(8x-3)$
15. $(3x+4)(8x-5)$

16. $(3a-5)(2a+3)$
17. $(3t-2)(2t+1)$
18. $(3b-2)^2$
19. $(x-2y)(5x+3y)$
20. $(x-2)(4x-3)$

EXERCISE 12m
1. $(2x+5)(2x-5)$
2. $(3x+2)(3x-2)$
3. $(6a+1)(6a-1)$

4. $(4a+b)(4a-b)$
5. $(3x+5)(3x-5)$
6. $(2a+1)(2a-1)$

7. $(4a+3b)(4a-3b)$
8. $(5s+3t)(5s-3t)$
9. $(10x+7y)(10x-7y)$
10. $(3y+4z)(3y-4z)$

11. $(2x+7y)(2x-7y)$
12. $(9x+10y)(9x-10y)$
13. $(3a+2b)(3a-2b)$
14. $(8p+9q)(8p-9q)$

15. $3(a+3b)(a-3b)$
16. $2(3t+5s)(3t-5s)$
17. $3(3x+y)(3x-y)$

18. $5(3x+2)(3x-2)$

19. $5(a+2)(a-2)$
20. $5(3+b)(3-b)$
21. $\frac{1}{2}(a+2b)(a-2b)$

22. $\left(\dfrac{a}{2}+\dfrac{b}{3}\right)\left(\dfrac{a}{2}-\dfrac{b}{3}\right)$
or $\frac{1}{36}(3a+2b)(3a-2b)$

23. $\frac{1}{3}(9x+y)(9x-y)$

24. $\left(\dfrac{x}{4}+\dfrac{y}{5}\right)\left(\dfrac{x}{4}-\dfrac{y}{5}\right)$ or $\frac{1}{400}(5x+4y)(5x-4y)$

EXERCISE 12n
1. 7.5
2. 18.5
3. 17.7
4. 35.04

5. 31.2
6. 20.4
7. 12.9
8. 178.97

9. 1000
10. 336
11. 53.2
12. 5.336

13. 8
14. 140
15. 75.8
16. 0.526

EXERCISE 12p This is an important exercise. Forgetting to extract a common factor results in many expressions being more difficult to factorise than they need be.

1. $5(x+1)(3x+2)$
2. $2(x-2)(2x+1)$
3. $3(x+1)(2x+1)$
4. $3(x-2)(6x+5)$
5. $2(x+5)(4x-3)$

6. $2(x+1)(4x+3)$
7. $5(x-3)(5x+2)$
8. $3(x-1)(3x+4)$
9. $2(x+4)(3x+1)$
10. $5(x+4)(3x-2)$

11. $2(3x-2)(3x-4)$
12. $3(2x-1)(8x-1)$
13. $2(2x+1)(3x+2)$

14. $5(4x-3)(5x-2)$
15. $4(2x+1)(3x-2)$
16. $7(x+4)(3x-2)$

17. $(4+3x)(1-2x)$
18. $(4-3x)(3+4x)$
19. $(7-x)(3+4x)$
20. $2(2-x)(6-x)$
21. $2(4+x)(2-3x)$

22. $(9-x)(1+x)$
23. $(12+x)(1-x)$
24. $2(2+3x)^2$
25. $5(3-x)^2$
26. $5(2+x)(2+3x)$

EXERCISE 12q
1. $(x+5)(x+8)$
2. $(3x+1)(2x+1)$
3. $(x+6)(x-6)$
4. Does not factorise

5. $(x-2)(x-6)$
6. $(2x-3)(x+5)$
7. $(x+7)(x-1)$
8. $(5x-2)(x+1)$

9. $(x-3)(x-8)$
10. $(3x+2)(x+3)$
11. $(x+15)(x-1)$
12. $(4x-1)(3x-1)$

13. $(x+2)(x+6)$
14. $(4x+1)(2x-1)$
15. $(x+7)(x-7)$
16. Does not factorise

17. $(3x+2)(2x-5)$
18. $(x+6)(x+7)$
19. $(2x+3y)(2x-3y)$
20. $(5x-4)(3x-2)$

21. $(2x-3)(3x+2)$
22. $(x+13)(x-2)$
23. $2(3x+1)(5x-2)$
24. $(4+x)(7-x)$

25. $(2x-1)(3x+4)$
26. $5(2x+1)(3x+2)$
27. $(x+2)(x+9)$
28. $(x-4)(x-6)$

29. $4(x+2y)(x-2y)$
30. Does not factorise
31. $2(3x+2)(2x-5)$
32. $(x-2)(x+15)$

33. $(2-x)(14+x)$
34. $(a-7)(a-9)$
35. $2(3-2x)(1-2x)$
36. $(1+2x)(1+4x^2)$

37. $(x+17)(x-4)$
38. $(2x-1)(x^3+2)$
39. $3(2x+1)(x-2)$
40. $(p+1)(p^2+1)$

41. $(a+b+c)(a+b-c)$
42. $(29x+1)(4x-1)$
43. $(a+16)(a+7)$
44. $(x^2+y+1)(x^2-y-1)$

45. $(a-8)(3a-7)$
46. $2(x+7)(x-11)$
47. $(2x+y-z)(2x-y+z)$
48. $(ab+18)(ab-19)$

EXERCISE 12r
1. a) $7a+21$ 　　b) $3x-6y$
2. a) $x^2+14x+40$ 　　b) $6x^2-19x+15$
3. a) $25+10x+x^2$ 　　b) $25-10x+x^2$ 　　c) $25-x^2$
4. a) $10(a+2)$ 　　b) $5p(3p-2)$
5. a) $(a+1)(a^2+1)$ 　　b) $(k+l)(2m-n)$
6. a) $(x-3)(x+9)$ 　　b) $(x-7)(5x-7)$ 　　c) $\left(a+\dfrac{b}{2}\right)\left(a-\dfrac{b}{2}\right)$
7. a) $(5x+2)(2x-3)$ 　　b) $(10a+9b)(10a-9b)$

EXERCISE 12s
1. a) $5a^2+15a$ 　　b) $12x^2-8xy$
2. a) $y^2-9y+20$ 　　b) $15x^2-14xy-8y^2$
3. a) $4p^2+12pq+9q^2$ 　　b) $4p^2-12pq+9q^2$ 　　c) $4p^2-9q^2$
4. a) $4z^2(2z-1)$ 　　b) $5y(x-4z)$
5. a) $(m+1)(2+3n)$ 　　b) $(a+2b)(c-2d)$
6. a) $(x+3)(x-9)$ 　　b) $(4x-1)(x+7)$ 　　c) $(2m+9n)(2m-9n)$
7. a) $3(x-3)(5x-3)$ 　　b) Does not factorise or $5(3+5x-4x^2)$

EXERCISE 12t
1. a) $4a + 28$ b) $6x^2 - 9xy$
2. a) $x^2 + 12x + 27$ b) $15x^2 - x - 2$
3. a) $25x^2 + 20x + 4$ b) $25x^2 - 20x + 4$ c) $25x^2 - 4$
4. a) $6z(2z - 1)$ b) $4y(2x - 3z)$
5. a) $(z + 2)(z^2 + 1)$ b) $(3a + b)(c + 2)$
6. a) $(x - 6)(x + 4)$ b) $(2a + 5)(2a - 3)$ c) $\left(3m + \dfrac{n}{3}\right)\left(3m - \dfrac{n}{3}\right)$
7. a) $(5x - 3)(3x + 2)$ b) $(3 + 5x)(2 - 3x)$

CHAPTER 13   Quadratic Equations

This chapter introduces quadratic equations and covers solution by factorisation. Graphical solution, completing the square and using the formula are in Book 4A.

Many of the questions in the first two exercises can be considered orally. They form a useful introduction. It is also worth pointing out that if $A \times B = 0$ then stating that either $A = 0$ or $B = 0$ does not rule out the possibility that both A and B are zero.

EXERCISE 13a
1. a) 8 b) 0 c) 0   6. a) 33 b) 0 c) 0
2. a) 0 b) 5 c) 0   7. a) -24 b) 0 c) 0
3. a) 0 b) 7 c) 0   8. a) 70 b) 0 c) 0
4. a) 0 b) 0 c) 3   9. a) 0 b) 0 c) 20
5. a) 20 b) 0 c) 6   10. a) -9 b) 0 c) 0

EXERCISE 13b
1. 0   7. 0   13. a) 0 b) 0
2. 0   8. 2   14. a) 0 b) 0
3. 0   9. 0   15. a) 0 b) 0
4. any value   10. 7   16. a) 0 b) any value
5. 4   11. any value
6. 1   12. 0

17. $a = 0$ or $b = 1$ 22. $a = 0$ or $b = 4$
18. $a = 0$ or $b = 5$ 23. $a = 0$ or $b = 10$
19. $a = 0$ or $b = 2$ 24. $a = 1$ or $b = 0$
20. $a = 3$ or $b = 0$ 25. $a = 7$ or $b = 0$
21. $a = 9$ or $b = 0$ 26. $a = 12$ or $b = 0$

EXERCISE 13c
1. 0 or 3   6. 0 or 6
2. 0 or 5   7. 0 or 10
3. 0 or 3   8. 0 or 7
4. 0 or -4 9. 0 or -7
5. 0 or -5 10. 0 or -9

11. 1, 2
12. 5 or 9
13. 7 or 10
14. 4 or 7
15. 1 or 6

16. 8 or -11
17. 3 or -5
18. -7 or 2
19. -2 or -3
20. -4 or -9

21. -1 or -8
22. p or q
23. $-a$ or -6
24. 4 or -1
25. -9 or 8

26. -6 or -7
27. -10 or -11
28. a or b
29. $-a$ or 6
30. c or $-d$

EXERCISE 13d
1. 1 or $2\frac{1}{2}$
2. 4 or $\frac{2}{3}$
3. $\frac{4}{5}$ or $\frac{3}{4}$
4. 0 or $1\frac{1}{4}$
5. 0 or $\frac{3}{10}$
6. $-\frac{2}{5}$ or 7
7. $-\frac{5}{6}$ or $\frac{2}{3}$
8. $\frac{3}{8}$ or $-2\frac{1}{2}$
9. $1\frac{1}{7}$ or $-3\frac{3}{4}$
10. $-\frac{3}{4}$ or $-1\frac{1}{2}$

11. $2\frac{1}{3}$ or 2
12. $1\frac{2}{3}$ or $\frac{1}{2}$
13. 0 or $\frac{1}{3}$
14. 0 or $\frac{3}{7}$
15. $-1\frac{1}{2}$ or 3
16. $-\frac{3}{4}$ or $2\frac{1}{2}$
17. $-\frac{9}{10}$ or $\frac{4}{5}$
18. $\frac{2}{3}$ or $-2\frac{1}{4}$
19. $2\frac{2}{5}$ or $-3\frac{1}{2}$
20. $-1\frac{3}{5}$ or $-\frac{3}{4}$

EXERCISE 13e
1. 1 or 2
2. 1 or 7
3. 2 or 3
4. 2 or 5
5. 3 or 4

6. 1 or 5
7. 1 or 11
8. 2 or 4
9. 2 or 6
10. 1 or 12

11. 1 or -7
12. 4 or -2
13. 3 or -4
14. 5 or -3
15. 2 or -9

16. -1 or 13
17. 2 or -3
18. -2 or 6
19. 4 or -5
20. -3 or 8

21. -1 or -2
22. -1 or -7
23. -3 or -5
24. -2 or -6
25. -2 or -9

26. -1 or -6
27. -2 or -5
28. -1 or -13
29. -1 or -15
30. -3 or -6

31. ±1
32. ±3
33. ±4
34. ±9
35. ±13

36. ±2
37. ±5
38. ±10
39. ±12
40. ±6

EXERCISE 13f
1. 0 or 2
2. 0 or 10
3. 0 or -8
4. 0 or $\frac{1}{2}$
5. 0 or $\frac{5}{4}$

6. 0 or 5
7. 0 or -3
8. 0 or -1
9. 0 or $\frac{5}{3}$
10. 0 or $\frac{7}{5}$

11. 0 or $-\frac{3}{2}$
12. 0 or $-\frac{5}{8}$
13. 0 or 7
14. 0 or $-\frac{5}{3}$
15. 0 or $\frac{12}{7}$

16. 0 or $-\frac{7}{6}$
17. 0 or $-\frac{7}{12}$
18. 0 or -4
19. 0 or $\frac{2}{7}$
20. 0 or $-\frac{3}{14}$

EXERCISE 13g
1. 1 (twice)
2. 5 (twice)
3. 10 (twice)
4. -4 (twice)
5. -3 (twice)

6. 3 (twice)
7. 4 (twice)
8. 9 (twice)
9. -1 (twice)
10. -10 (twice)

11. -9 (twice)
12. 7 (twice)
13. 11 (twice)
14. -6 (twice)
15. $\frac{1}{2}$ (twice)

16. -5 (twice)
17. 6 (twice)
18. 20 (twice)
19. 8 (twice)
20. $-\frac{2}{3}$ (twice)

EXERCISE 13h
1. $\frac{1}{2}$ and 2
2. $1\frac{1}{2}$ and 4
3. $2\frac{1}{2}$ and 4
4. -1 and $-\frac{2}{3}$
5. -7 and $2\frac{1}{2}$

6. $\frac{2}{3}$ and 3
7. $\frac{1}{3}$ and 2
8. $1\frac{1}{2}$ and -4
9. $-\frac{2}{3}$ and -3
10. $-\frac{2}{5}$ and -5

11. $-\frac{1}{2}$ and $\frac{2}{3}$
12. $\frac{2}{5}$ and $-1\frac{1}{3}$
13. $\frac{1}{3}$ and $\frac{1}{4}$
14. $-\frac{1}{3}$ and $2\frac{1}{2}$
15. $-\frac{1}{5}$ and $-\frac{3}{4}$

16. $\frac{3}{4}$ and $1\frac{1}{2}$
17. $-\frac{5}{6}$ and $2\frac{1}{2}$
18. $-\frac{1}{2}$ and $-1\frac{1}{2}$
19. $-\frac{2}{3}$ and $-\frac{3}{4}$
20. $3\frac{1}{2}$ and $-\frac{3}{5}$

21. $\pm\frac{5}{4}$
22. $\pm\frac{9}{10}$
23. $\pm\frac{5}{2}$
24. $\pm\frac{4}{3}$
25. $\pm\frac{12}{5}$

26. $\pm\frac{2}{3}$
27. $\pm\frac{5}{9}$
28. $\pm\frac{2}{5}$
29. $\pm\frac{5}{6}$
30. $\pm\frac{9}{2}$

EXERCISE 13i
1. -5 and 6
2. -2 and 8
3. 3 and -12
4. $\frac{2}{3}$ and -2

5. 3 and -2
6. 1 and -7
7. $\frac{1}{2}$ and -3
8. 3 and $-\frac{3}{5}$

9. 3 or -1
10. -4 and 6
11. 5 and 7
12. $-\frac{1}{5}$ or $1\frac{1}{2}$

13. -2 and 5
14. 2 and 4
15. $\frac{1}{2}$ and $-\frac{1}{3}$
16. $\frac{1}{3}$ and 4

17. 2 and 5
18. 1 and 7
19. 2 and 4
20. 3 and 7

21. 2 and 6
22. 4 and 5
23. 5 and 7
24. 3 and 5

25. 0 and $\frac{1}{2}$
26. 2 and 3
27. 2 and 6
28. -1 and $-\frac{2}{3}$
29. $\frac{1}{2}$ and -3

30. 0 and 3
31. 1 and 2
32. -1 and -2
33. $\frac{1}{3}$ and 2
34. $-\frac{1}{5}$ and $1\frac{1}{2}$

EXERCISE 13j
1. -4 and 5
2. 2 (twice)
3. $\pm\frac{1}{3}$
4. 0 and $-3\frac{1}{2}$

5. -1 and -12
6. $\pm\frac{1}{4}$
7. 0 and 6
8. -5 and 7

9. 2 and $-3\frac{1}{2}$
10. -3 (twice)
11. 1 and -7
12. $\pm\frac{2}{5}$

13. $\pm2\frac{1}{2}$
14. -2 and -9
15. $\frac{1}{2}$ and $-\frac{2}{3}$
16. 0 and $2\frac{1}{2}$

17. 2 and $-\frac{1}{3}$

18. $-\frac{1}{2}$ and $-1\frac{1}{3}$

19. 0 and $1\frac{3}{4}$

20. $\frac{1}{3}$ and $\frac{1}{4}$

21. $\frac{1}{3}$ and $-2\frac{1}{2}$

22. $-\frac{1}{3}$ and 2

23. $-\frac{1}{2}$ and $-1\frac{1}{2}$

24. $\pm\frac{1}{2}$

25. 3 and -4

26. 3 and -1

27. $\frac{1}{2}$ and $-\frac{1}{3}$

28. 1 and 4

29. -3 and 8

30. 5 and 7

31. -2 and $\frac{2}{3}$

32. $-\frac{1}{3}$ and 2

33. 5 and -10

34. -11 and 8

35. 5 and -9

36. -2 and 7

37. 7 and -4

38. 5 and -11

39. -4 and -5

40. -4 and -5

41. 0, 1 and 2

42. 0, 3 and -4

43. 0, 2 and $2\frac{1}{2}$

44. 0, 1 and 1

45. 0, $-\frac{1}{2}$ and -4

46. 0, 6 and 7

47. 0, -2 and 5

48. 0, 5 and $-2\frac{1}{3}$

49. 0, $\frac{3}{2}$ and $-\frac{3}{2}$

50. 0, 2 and 4

EXERCISE 13k Above average candidates should find a great deal of satisfaction from this exercise.

1. -2 or 8   **2.** -2 or 7   **3.** -7 or 6

4. $x + (x^2 - 6) = 66$; $x = -9$ or 8; 8 marbles

5. $x + x^2 = 56$; $x = -8$ or 7; Ahmed is 7 and his father is 49

6. $x + (x^2 + 2) = 44$; $x = -7$ or 6; Kathryn is 6 and her mother is 38

7. $x(x + 5) = 84$; $x = 7$ or -12; Peter is 7

8. $x(x - 4) = 140$; $x = 14$ or -10; Ann is 10

9. $x(x + 3) = 28$; $x = 4$ or -7; 4 cm by 7 cm

10. $x(x + 5) = 66$; $x = -11$ or 6; 6 cm by 11 cm

11. $\frac{1}{2}x \times \frac{1}{2}x = 25$; $x = \pm 10$; 5 cm

12. a) $A = 20x\,\text{m}^2$, $B = x^2\,\text{m}^2$, $C = 30x\,\text{m}^2$

b) $x^2 + 50x = 104$; $x = 2$ or -52; path is 2 m wide

EXERCISE 13l

1. a) -10 b) 0   c) 8

2. a) 0 or -7 b) 0 or $\frac{1}{2}$

3. a) 3 and 8   b) 2 and $-\frac{3}{5}$

4. a) 7 and -5 b) 5 and 8

5. a) $\frac{1}{2}$ and $\frac{4}{5}$ b) $\frac{2}{5}$ and $-\frac{1}{3}$ c) $\pm\frac{2}{3}$

6. a) 0 and 2   b) 0 and $\frac{3}{4}$

7. a) $-\frac{1}{3}$ and $\frac{2}{3}$ b) $\frac{1}{2}$ and $2\frac{1}{3}$

8. a) 5 and -9 b) 5 and -6

EXERCISE 13m **1.** a) -2 b) 0 c) 12 d) 0

2. a) 0 and 2 b) 0 and $-\frac{3}{7}$

3. a) 2 and -5 b) -2 and $1\frac{1}{3}$ c) $-1\frac{1}{2}$ and $1\frac{1}{2}$

4. a) -3 and 2 b) -5 and -6

5. a) $\frac{1}{5}$ and $-\frac{3}{4}$ b) $-\frac{2}{5}$ and $-2\frac{1}{3}$

6. a) 0 and $-\frac{2}{3}$ b) 0 and $-\frac{3}{7}$

7. a) 5 and $-\frac{3}{4}$ b) $-\frac{1}{2}$ and $2\frac{1}{3}$

8. a) -4 and 8 b) -2 and 4

EXERCISE 13n **1.** a) -11 b) 0 c) 0

2. a) 0, -7 b) 0, $\frac{3}{4}$

3. a) $-4, 5$ b) $1\frac{3}{4}, -3$ c) $\frac{3}{5}, -\frac{3}{5}$

4. a) $5, -3$ b) $-4, -8$

5. a) $-\frac{1}{5}, -\frac{3}{4}$ b) $-\frac{2}{7}, \frac{1}{4}$

6. a) $0, -1\frac{1}{3}$ b) $0, -1\frac{2}{3}$

7. a) $\frac{2}{7}, -1$ b) $-\frac{1}{2}, 1\frac{2}{3}$

8. a) $-5, 2$ b) $-10, 3$

CHAPTER 14 Graphs

This chapter concentrates on the practical aspect of graphs—drawing acceptable curves, making up tables from formulae and reading values from the graph.

It is worth starting by showing some examples of graphs which give a misleading impression. For example, ask pupils what these graphs show:

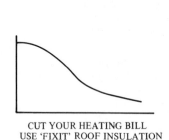

CUT YOUR HEATING BILL
USE 'FIXIT' ROOF INSULATION

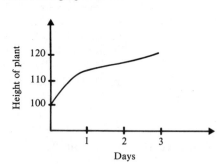

Ask the pupils to bring in some examples of graphs from magazines etc., for discussion.

We have used a dot within a circle $\odot$ to mark points on a graph. Some may prefer to use a cross, i.e. $\times$ or $+$.

In early graphical work some pupils may fail to draw a satisfactory curve first time. It would be wiser to get them to re-draw it on a fresh sheet, using the benefit of the first unsatisfactory attempt, than to rush on to a new question. While a few pupils will be most unlikely to draw an acceptable curve, most pupils' graphical work can be improved significantly by careful attention to the section headed "Points to remember when drawing graphs of curves".

EXERCISE 14a
1. a) $200t$ b) $3.16\,\mathrm{cm}$ 4. a) $3\,\mathrm{cm}$ b) $67\,\mathrm{cm}^2$
2. a) £168.9   b) 7.27 years   5. a) $16.5\,\mathrm{cm}$ b) 2.21
3. a) 3.6   b) 2.3

EXERCISE 14b
1. a) $59.5\,\mathrm{m}$ b) $4.47\,\mathrm{s}$ 4. 2.65, 5.29
2. a) 4.8   b) 7.5   5. a) 3.33   b) -1.43
3. a) 1.67   b) 1.09

EXERCISE 14c For the most able it is worth pointing out that they are using their graphs to solve quadratic equations.

1. The graph passes through the origin O, which is also the lowest value for y.
2. a) 1.73 or -1.73 b) No
3. a) 2 and -2 b) 1 and -1, Yes
4. They all have the same shape.
   They all have the same shape but cross the y-axis at different points.
5. a) When $x = 0$ and $x = 3$ b) -0.79 and 3.79
6. a) When $x = 0$ and 1.5   b) $-1\frac{1}{8}$ when $x = \frac{3}{4}$
7. a) -2 when $x = -1$ b) 10.5   c) 0 and -2
8. a) -4 when $x = 1$
   b) (i) -1.24 and 3.24   (ii) -2.46 and 4.46
9. a) 6.25 when $x = 0.5$
   b) (i) -2.37 and 3.37   (ii) -1 and 2

CHAPTER 15 Polygons

This chapter starts with the sum of the exterior angles and then deduces the sum of the interior angles. Some teachers may prefer to do this the other way round and here are two methods:

1. Building polygons up from triangles:

Number of sides = number of triangles -2
So the sum of the interior angles of an n-sided polygon
$\quad\quad\quad\quad = $ the sum of the interior angles of $(n-2)$ triangles
$\quad\quad\quad\quad = (n-2)\ 180°$

2. Taking a point inside a polygon:

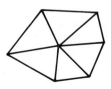

An n-sided polygon gives n triangles
So the sum of the interior angles of the polygon
$\quad\quad\quad\quad = $ the sum of the interior angles of n triangles $-$ angle sum at P
$\quad\quad\quad\quad = (180n-360)°$

EXERCISE 15a
1. No, angles not equal

2. Yes

3. No, sides not equal

4. No, $\begin{cases} \text{sides not equal} \\ \text{angles not equal} \end{cases}$

5. No, $\begin{cases} \text{sides not equal} \\ \text{angles not equal} \end{cases}$

6. No, $\begin{cases} \text{sides not equal} \\ \text{angles not equal} \end{cases}$

7. Yes

8. No, not bounded by straight lines

EXERCISE 15b
1. $180°$
2. $360°$
3. a) $p = 100°$, $r = 135°$, $x = 55°$, $q = 125°$ b) $360°$
4. a) $w = 120°$, $x = 60°$, $y = 120°$, $z = 60°$ b) $360°$
5. a) $180°$ b) $540°$ c) $180°$ d) $360°$
6. $360°$
7. a) equilateral   b) $60°$ c) $120°$ d) $60°$ e) $360°$

EXERCISE 15c To demonstrate the sum of the exterior angles, a ruler can be placed along one side and then slid and turned until it is back to its original position.

1. $60°$
2. $90°$
3. $50°$
4. $50°$
5. $60°$

6. $90°$
7. $95°$
8. $55°$
9. $30°$
10. $125°$

11. $x = 50°$
12. $x = 30°$
13. $x = 24°$
14. a) 5   b) 8

EXERCISE 15d
1. $36°$
2. $45°$
3. $30°$

4. $60°$
5. $24°$
6. $20°$

7. $40°$
8. $22.5°$
9. $18°$

EXERCISE 15e

1. 720°	**4.** 360°	**7.** 2880°
2. 540°	**5.** 900°	**8.** 1260°
3. 1440°	**6.** 1800°	**9.** 2340°

EXERCISE 15f

1. a) 3240°   b) 2520°   c) 1620°

2. 80°	**4.** 110°	**6.** 85°
3. 120°	**5.** 105°	**7.** 110°

8. 108°	**10.** 135°	**12.** 150°
9. 120°	**11.** 144°	**13.** 162°

14. a) 18   b) 24   **15.** a) 12   b) 20
16. a) yes, 12   b) yes, 9   c) no   d) yes, 6   e) no   f) yes, 4
17. a) yes, 4   b) yes, 6   c) no   d) yes, 72   e) yes, 36   f) yes, 8

EXERCISE 15g In Numbers 15–20 the most able should give reasoned answers. In many cases the teacher may decide that symmetry is acceptable.

1. 54°	**6.** 50°	**11.** 72°	**15.** a) 36°	b) 36°
2. 45°	**7.** 80°	**12.** 45°	**16.** a) 128.6°	b) 25.7°
3. 150°	**8.** 135°	**13.** 60°	**17.** 77.1°	
4. 72°	**9.** 100°	**14.** 36°	**18.** a) 22.5°	b) 22.5°
5. 60°	**10.** 60°		**19.** 22.5°	
			20. 45°	

EXERCISE 15h Number 6 can be used to take the idea of tessellations further, i.e. some shapes built up from squares and equilateral triangles will tessellate. For example:

After tessellations with shapes that *do* work, pupils can try these two shapes (which do not tessellate)

and then investigate some shapes of their own.

1. a) The interior angles (135°) do not divide exactly into 360°
   b) A square
2. a) No   b) A regular ten-sided polygon
4. Square, equilateral triangle

CHAPTER 16 Matrix Transformations ▬▬▬▬▬▬▬

Squared paper can be used for this chapter.

EXERCISE 16a 1. $\begin{pmatrix} 4 \\ 5 \end{pmatrix}$ 3. $\begin{pmatrix} -7 \\ 5 \end{pmatrix}$ 5. $\begin{pmatrix} 5 \\ 3 \end{pmatrix}$

2. $\begin{pmatrix} 3 \\ -2 \end{pmatrix}$ 4. $\begin{pmatrix} -3 \\ -5 \end{pmatrix}$ 6. $\begin{pmatrix} -5 \\ 2 \end{pmatrix}$

7. $(5, 2)$ 9. $(-2, -4)$ 11. $(-6, 2)$
8. $(1, -3)$ 10. $(2, -3)$ 12. $(2, -6)$

EXERCISE 16b The drawings are clearer if the objects are drawn in one colour and the images in another.

1. $\begin{pmatrix} 2 \\ -5 \end{pmatrix}$ 3. $\begin{pmatrix} -4 \\ 2 \end{pmatrix}$ 5. $\begin{pmatrix} 3 \\ 5 \end{pmatrix}$

2. $\begin{pmatrix} -4 \\ -3 \end{pmatrix}$ 4. $\begin{pmatrix} 5 \\ 3 \end{pmatrix}$ 6. $\begin{pmatrix} 4 \\ 2 \end{pmatrix}$

EXERCISE 16c 1. $\begin{pmatrix} 5 \\ 11 \end{pmatrix}$ 3. $\begin{pmatrix} 4 \\ 1 \end{pmatrix}$ 5. $\begin{pmatrix} 5 \\ 4 \end{pmatrix}$

2. $\begin{pmatrix} 9 \\ 6 \end{pmatrix}$ 4. $\begin{pmatrix} -2 \\ -5 \end{pmatrix}$ 6. $\begin{pmatrix} -1 \\ -1 \end{pmatrix}$

7. A′(−1, 1), B′(−3, 2)   10. A′(3, 3), B′(−6, 0)
8. A′(−1, −1), B′(2, 4)   11. A′(−3, 2), B′(3, −7)
9. A′(10, 3), B′(−5, −2)   12. A′(7, 4), B′(1, −8)

EXERCISE 16d There are only four commonly used reflections so some of them are bound to crop up twice. This could encourage the pupils to notice that the same transformation can act on two different objects to produce two different images but the *transformation* is still the same.

1. A′(−2, −1), B′(2, −1), C′(3, −2), D′(−1, −2); Reflection in x-axis
2. A′(1, 1), B′(1, 4), C′(2, 4); Reflection in line $y = x$
3. A′(−2, −3), B′(−5, −3), C′(−3, 2); Reflection in y-axis
4. A′(−1, −4), B′(−3, −3), C′(0, −2); Reflection in line $y = -x$
5. A′(1, 1), B′(1, 3), C′(2, 3), D′(2, 1); Reflection in line $y = x$
6. A′(0, 2), B′(0, 4), C′(2, 4), D′(2, 2); Reflection in line $y = x$
7. A′(−1, −1), B′(−1, −2), C′(−2, −2), D′(−2, −1); Reflection in line $y = -x$

8. A′(−1, 0), B′(−4, 0), C′(−4, 2); Reflection in y-axis

9. A′(2, −1), B′(3, −1), C′(3, −4), D′(2, −4); Reflection in x-axis

10. A′(1, 1), B′(1, 3), C′(3, 4), D′(3, 3); Reflection in line $y = x$

11. A′(−2, 4), B′(−4, 5), C′(−3, 2); Reflection in y-axis

EXERCISE 16e **1.** A′(1, −1), B′(1, −4), C′(3, −4), D′(3, −1); Rotation of 90° clockwise about O

2. A′(−1, −1), B′(−4, −1), C′(−4, −2), D′(−1, −2); Rotation of 180° about O

3. A′(0, 1), B′(0, 3), C′(−4, 4); Rotation of 90° anticlockwise about O

4. A′(1, −1), B′(1, −4), C′(4, −4); Rotation of 90° clockwise about O

5. A′(−3, −2), B′(−4, −3), C′(−1, −4); Rotation of 180° about O

EXERCISE 16f **1.** A′(2, 0), B′(6, 0), C′(6, 6); Enlargement centre O, scale factor 2

2. A′(0, 3), B′(−6, 3), C′(−6, 0), O′(0, 0); Enlargement centre O, scale factor 3

3. A′(3, 3), B′(3, 6), C′(6, 6), D′(6, 3); Enlargement centre O, scale factor $1\frac{1}{2}$

4. A′(10, 5), B′(10, 10), C′(−10, 10); Enlargement centre O, scale factor $2\frac{1}{2}$

5. O′(0, 0), A′(0, −2), B′(2, −2), C′(+2, 0); Enlargement centre O, scale factor −2

6. A′(0, −2), B′(−3, −2), C′(−3, −5), D′(0, −5); Enlargement centre O, scale factor −1

EXERCISE 16g **1.** A′(3, 0), B′(9, 0), C′(9, 2), D′(3, 2); Stretch parallel to x-axis, scale factor 3

2. A′(1, 0), B′(3, 0), C′(3, 4), D′(1, 4); Stretch parallel to y-axis, scale factor 2

3. A′($1\frac{1}{2}$, 1), B′(6, 1), C′(6, 2), D′($1\frac{1}{2}$, 2); Stretch parallel to x-axis, scale factor $1\frac{1}{2}$

4. A′(−2, 3), B′(1, 3), C′(1, 6), D′(1, 6); Stretch parallel to y-axis, scale factor 3

EXERCISE 16h **1.** A′(−2, 0), B′(2, 0), C′(4, 2), D′(0, 2); Shear, invariant line the x-axis, (2, 2) → (4, 2)

2. A′(0, 1), B′(2, 5), C′(2, 6), D′(0, 2); Shear, invariant line the y-axis, (2, 2) → (2, 6)

3. A′(1, 0), B′(3, 0), C′(6, 2); Shear, invariant line the x-axis, (2, 2) → (6, 2)

4. A′(−2, 0), B′(2, 0), C′(−2, 2), D′(−6, 2); Shear, invariant line the x-axis, (2, 2) → (−2, 2)

5. A′(0, 1), B′(3, 4), C′(3, 5), D′(0, 2); Shear, invariant line the y-axis, (3, 2) → (3, 5)

6. A′(−1, 2), B′(2, −1), C′(2, 2), D′(−1, 5); Shear, invariant line the y-axis, (2, 4) → (2, 2)

7. A′(−2, −1), B′(1, −1), C′(2, 2); Shear, invariant line the x-axis, (0, 2) → (2, 2)

9. A′(−2, 1), B′(2, 1), C′(−1, 4), D′(−5, 4); Shear, invariant line the x-axis, (3, 1) → (2, 1)

10. A′(−1, 1), B′(1, 1), C′(5, 3), D′(3, 3); Shear, invariant line the x-axis, (−3, 1) → (−1, 1)

11. A′(−1, −3), B′(−1, 0), C′(−3, −4), D′(−3, −5); Shear, invariant line the y-axis, (−1, −1) → (−1, −3)

12. A′(−4, 2), B′(−1, 2), C′(−5, 4), D′(−8, 4); Shear, invariant line the y-axis, (0, 2) → (−4, 2)

EXERCISE 16i   **1.** A′(−1, −3), B′(1, 3), C′(5, 5), D′(3, −1); (Parallelogram)

2. A′(−1, 3), B′(1, −3), C′(−3, −1), D′(−5, 5); (Parallelogram)

3. A′(−4, −3), B′(2, −3), C′(2, 6), D′(−4, 6); (Rectangle)

4. A′(−8, −4), B′(−2, −1), C′(6, 3), D′(0, 0); (Straight line)

5. A′(1, −2), B′(−3, 6), C′(−1, 2), D′(3, −6); (Straight line)

6. All points → the origin

EXERCISE 16j   In Number 16, we can see that the images of $\overrightarrow{OA}$ and $\overrightarrow{OB}$ are given by the columns of the transformation matrix, because $\begin{pmatrix} 1 & 2 \\ 0 & 1 \end{pmatrix}\begin{pmatrix} 1 & 0 \\ 0 & 1 \end{pmatrix} = \begin{pmatrix} 1 & 2 \\ 0 & 1 \end{pmatrix}$.

A diagram showing the object and the image may therefore be drawn without any calculation. However, not all pupils can recognise the transformation from a diagram showing the position vectors of A, B, A′ and B′ only.

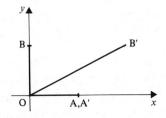

If a transformation has to be identified, the unit square of Number 13 is the best object to choose to use.

1. O′(0, 0), A′(2, 0), B′(2, −1), C′(0, −1); Reflection in x-axis

2. O′(0, 0), A′(2, 0), B′(3½, 1), C′(1½, 1); Shear, invariant line the x-axis, (2, 1) → (3½, 1)

3. O′(0, 0), A′(0, −2), B′(−1, −2), C′(−1, 0); Reflection in line y = −x

4. O′(0, 0), A′(−6, 0), B′(−6, 3), C′(0, 3)

5. O′(0, 0), A′(4, 6), B′(1, 8), C′(−3, 2)

6. O′(0, 0), A′(4, 0), B′(4, 1), C′(0, 1); Stretch parallel to the x-axis, scale factor 2

7. O′(0, 0), A′(8, 0), B′(8, 4), C′(0, 4); Enlargement centre O, scale factor 4

8. O′(0, 0), A′(2, 2), B′(4, 6), C′(2, 4)

9. O′(0, 0), A′(2, 0), B′(2, 3), C′(0, 3); Stretch parallel to the y-axis, scale factor 3

10. O′(0, 0), A′(1, 0), B′(1, ½), C′(0, ½); Enlargement centre O, scale factor ½

11. O′(0, 0), A′(4, 2), B′(6, 5), C′(2, 3)

12. O′(0, 0), A′(2, 4), B′(2, 5), C′(0, 1); Shear, invariant line the y-axis, (2, 1) → (2, 5)

13. The unit square OABC; A(1, 0), B(1, 1), C(0, 1); or the unit triangle OAB

14.

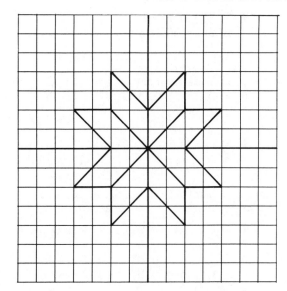

15. The image is the same as the object in each case

16. a) A'(1, 0), B'(0, −1)   b) A'(2, 0), B'(0, 2)
c) A'(1, 0), B'(2, 1)   d) A'(2, 4), B'(5, −1)
The columns of the matrices give the position vectors of A' and B'

EXERCISE 16k
1. Rotation of 90° anticlockwise about the origin
2. Enlargement centre O and scale factor $\frac{1}{3}$
3. Reflection in the x-axis
4. Rotation of 45° clockwise about the origin

EXERCISE 16l
1. a) A'(0, 1), B'(0, 3), C'(−3, 3)
    b) Rotation of 90° anticlockwise about the origin
    c) $\begin{pmatrix} 0 & 1 \\ -1 & 0 \end{pmatrix}$ d) The image is ABC
    e) Rotation of 90° clockwise about the origin

2. a) A'(3, 3), B'(6, 3), C'(6, 6), D'(3, 6)
    b) Enlargement centre O, with scale factor 3
    c) $\begin{pmatrix} \frac{1}{3} & 0 \\ 0 & \frac{1}{3} \end{pmatrix}$ d) The image is ABCD
    e) Enlargement centre O, scale factor $\frac{1}{3}$; Yes

3. a) A'(0, −1), B'(1, −3), C'(2, −3), D'(1, −1)
    b) Rotation of 90° clockwise about the origin
    c) $\begin{pmatrix} 0 & -1 \\ 1 & 0 \end{pmatrix}$ d) The image is ABCD
    e) Rotation of 90° anticlockwise about the origin. Yes

4. a) A'(3, 1), B'(9, 3), C'(7, 3)

b) Shear, invariant line the x-axis, $(1, 1) \rightarrow (3, 1)$

c) $\begin{pmatrix} 1 & -2 \\ 0 & 1 \end{pmatrix}$ d) The image is ABC

e) Shear, invariant line the x-axis, $(3, 1) \rightarrow (1, 1)$; Yes

5. a) A'(1, 3), B'(3, 9), C'(5, 13), D'(3, 7)

b) $\begin{pmatrix} -2 & 1 \\ 3 & -1 \end{pmatrix}$ c) A'B'C'D' $\rightarrow$ ABCD

6. a) O'(0, 0), A'(2, 1), B'(10, 5), C'(8, 4); Image is a straight line

b) No inverse   c) Transformation has no inverse either

EXERCISE 16m The results of this exercise may already have been noticed during the previous work so this exercise may not be necessary.

1. O'(0, 0), A'(2, 0), B'(6, 2), C'(4, 2); O and A

2. O'(0, 0), A'(4, 0), B'(4, 4), C'(0, 4); O

3. O'(0, 0), A'(2, 0), B'(2, −2), C'(0, −2); O and A

4. O'(0, 0), A'(4, 2), B'(6, 6), C'(2, 4); O

5. The origin; Yes

EXERCISE 16n **1.** Translation defined by the vector $\begin{pmatrix} 5 \\ 1 \end{pmatrix}$

2. Translation defined by the vector $\begin{pmatrix} -5 \\ 1 \end{pmatrix}$

3. Translation defined by the vector $\begin{pmatrix} 3 \\ -4 \end{pmatrix}$

4. Translation defined by the vector $\begin{pmatrix} -4 \\ 0 \end{pmatrix}$

5. O'(3, 1), A'(4, 1), B'(4, 3), C'(3, 3)

6. A'(−1, −2), B'(−1, 0), C'(−2, 0)

7. A'(1, −1), B'(2, −1), C'(2, 1)

8. A'(0, 1), B'(1, 1), C'(1, 3), D'(0, 3)

9. Translations defined by the vectors:

1. $\begin{pmatrix} -5 \\ -1 \end{pmatrix}$ 2. $\begin{pmatrix} 5 \\ -1 \end{pmatrix}$ 3. $\begin{pmatrix} -3 \\ 4 \end{pmatrix}$ 4. $\begin{pmatrix} 4 \\ 0 \end{pmatrix}$

5. $\begin{pmatrix} -3 \\ -1 \end{pmatrix}$ 6. $\begin{pmatrix} 3 \\ 3 \end{pmatrix}$ 7. $\begin{pmatrix} -4 \\ 2 \end{pmatrix}$ 8. $\begin{pmatrix} 1 \\ -1 \end{pmatrix}$

CHAPTER 17   Ratio and Proportion

The first part of this chapter is revision of the work in Book 2, although problems with mixed units are dealt with more thoroughly here.

EXERCISE 17a
1. $2:3$
2. $1:2:3$
3. $7:5$
4. $2:3$
5. $18:8:9$
6. $2:3:1$
7. $4:9$
8. $3:5:4$
9. $2:3:1$

10. $6:11$
11. $15:4$
12. $31:4$
13. $5:16$

14. $1.5:1$
15. $2.4:1$
16. $0.857:1$
17. $2.73:1$
18. $0.6:1$
19. $2.63:1$
20. $1.33:1$
21. $0.75:1$
22. $1.43:1$

EXERCISE 17b
1. $9:2$
2. $2:5$
3. $17:60$
4. $2:125$
5. $9:20$
6. $50:3$

7. $20:19$
8. $36:35$
9. $27:25$
10. $9:10$

11. $25:24$
12. a) $3:2$ b) $2:3$ c) $3:5$

13. a) $2:3$ b) $9:5$ c) $21:23$ d) $6:5$

14. $18:25$
15. a) $1:1$ b) $1:2$ c) $1:8$ d) $1:1$ e) $1:3$ f) $1:8$

16. a) $1:9$ b) $1:4$ c) $4:9$

EXERCISE 17c
1. $1\frac{1}{9}$ or 1.11
2. $\frac{3}{7}$ or 0.429
3. $7\frac{1}{2}$ or 7.5
4. $1\frac{3}{7}$ or $1:43$
5. 24
6. $22\frac{1}{2}$

7. $9\frac{1}{3}$ or 9.33
8. $2\frac{8}{11}$ or 2.73
9. $1\frac{1}{5}$ or 1.2
10. $7\frac{1}{5}$ or 7.2
11. $3\frac{1}{3}$ or 3.33
12. $8\frac{4}{7}$ or 8.57

13. 12 grandsons; $3:7$
14. 152
15. $10.1\,\text{cm}$
16. 264

EXERCISE 17d
1. £20, £25
2. $54\,\text{m}$, $42\,\text{m}$
3. $0.625\,\text{kg}$, $1.25\,\text{kg}$, $3.125\,\text{kg}$
4. $\frac{1}{2}\,\text{hr}$, $2\frac{1}{2}\,\text{hrs}$, $4\,\text{hrs}$
5. 18 boys, 14 girls
6. $60°$, $50°$, $70°$
7. 9, 12, 9
8. 66 hits, 24 misses

EXERCISE 17e
1. $9:7$
2. $30\,\text{m}$, $42\,\text{m}$
3. $5\frac{1}{4}$
4. $2\frac{2}{9}$ or 2.22
5. $27.5\,\text{cm}$
6. $5:3$
7. $500:53$
8. $4:3$
9. $3:4$
10. $\frac{2}{3}$

Proportion: There are many different methods for dealing with problems on proportion but some of them are seen as black magic by the children.
Whichever method is used it should be used exclusively to avoid confusion.

Science and other subjects make great demands on the children's mathematical ability and particularly so in proportion problems, so it is as well for them to be familiar with the type of problem liable to crop up. They should also be prepared to use decimals as well as whole numbers.

The unitary method is based on the simplest idea but is not always the easiest to carry out and some people find the ratio method requires less work.

The third method is what some people call the "common sense" method, that is, to use a multiplying factor as in the following example:

At a steady speed a car uses 4 litres of petrol to travel 75 km. How much is needed for 60 km?

Amount needed $= 4 \times \dfrac{60}{75}$ km $\left(\text{we multiply by } \dfrac{60}{75} \text{ because } \textit{less} \text{ petrol is required}\right.$

to travel 60 km than 75 km $\Big)$.

However, deciding on the multiplying factor can cause worry, as "common sense" does not always come into play. (This method used to be called "the rule of three".)

EXERCISE 17f
1. a) £1.80   b) £7.20
2. a) 6 units   b) $\frac{3}{4}$ unit
3. a) 72 km   b) 118.8 km
4. a) 35 rows   b) 42 rows
5. a) £1.12$\frac{1}{2}$ b) £5.40

EXERCISE 17g
1. £1.20
2. 15.5 km
3. $4\frac{1}{3}$ or 4.33 km
4. 65 p
5. £7.70
6. £4.20
7. £8.30
8. 1.5 p
9. 1.5 m
10. 5.5 m^2

EXERCISE 17h
1. 3.2 litres
2. 3 hours
3. $12\frac{1}{2}$ units
4. 3.6 hours
5. a) £30   b) 350 miles
6. £96
7. 700
8. £2.64
9. 66 rows
10. 20.25 cm

11. £168
12. 480
13. 65.6 km
14. a) 2.25×10^7 b) 8.1×10^6 c) 1.35×10^5
15. 15 V
16. 24.7 joules
17. 41.8 p, 42 p
18. £14.05

Inverse Proportion: If a multiplying factor is used for direct proportion then it can also be used for inverse proportion, using common sense to decide which way up the factor should be. This method can only be used for numerical problems.

The unitary method is simpler than the ratio method for inverse proportion.

EXERCISE 17i **1.** $5\frac{1}{2}$ hours   **4.** 8 days   **7.** 16 cm

2. 12   **5.** 25 cm   **8.** 44

3. 203   **6.** 20   **9.** 49

EXERCISE 17j **1.** a) 10 350   b) 5.22   **7.** 24

2. £97.85   **8.** 34

3. $3\frac{1}{2}$ hours   **9.** 1.44 m

4. No answer   **10.** 6 weeks

5. 4.46 cm   **11.** No answer

6. 49   **12.** 1.5 amps

EXERCISE 17k **1.** 3 : 1   **5.** 6 hours 40 mins

2. $3\frac{3}{5}$ or 3.6   **6.** 6 : 2 : 1

3. 8 m, 16 m, 32 m   **7.** 9

4. 114 km (3 s.f.)   **8.** $\frac{6}{5}$: 1 or 1.2 : 1

EXERCISE 17l **1.** 4 : 3   **5.** 0.6 : 1

2. 12, 8, 20   **6.** £7.50

3. $6\frac{3}{5}$ or 6.6   **7.** 1 : 3

4. 8 : 7   **8.** £37.50

CHAPTER 18   Trigonometry

Exercises 18a to 18i repeat the work in Book 2 although there is a fuller introduction in Book 2 with work on drawing and measuring and on similar triangles.

All the exercises are suitable for use with calculators or with tables. The answers have been worked out on a calculator and angles are given in degrees correct to 1 decimal place. The notes that follow are points to consider with the various methods of calculation. The children will need a lot of practice and explanation of whichever method is used.

Use of tables: In some exercises the trigonometric ratios may need to be corrected to 3 decimal places for three figure tables or 4 decimal places for four figure tables.

Use of calculator: When two sides of a right-angled triangle are given, pupils using a calculator to find an angle can do so without a break to write down the value of the trig ratio. There are two reasons for discouraging this; firstly, many children cannot see their way through the complete calculation without the break; secondly, even if the calculation is done in one, the intermediate steps should be written down in case a mistake is made at the next stage. Some children make the jump from, for example, $\frac{x}{2} = \tan 20°$ to the value of x. This should be strictly discouraged as examining boards expect an explicit expression for x before the calculation, i.e. $x = 2\tan 20°$. When the intermediate step is written down, it is not sensible to write down all the figures from the display; the first four significant figures will give answers correct to three significant figures.

Degrees and minutes: If these are required then most tables have columns headed with minutes as well as with decimals of degrees. However, with four figure tables the side columns will have to be used to get answers to the nearest minute.

Calculators vary but some will give an angle in degrees and minutes if required. If necessary the decimal part of the angle can be multiplied by 60 to give minutes.

EXERCISE 18a
7. $\frac{5}{12}$, 0.4167   **10.** $\frac{3}{4}$, 0.75
8. $\frac{8}{15}$, 0.5333   **11.** $\frac{12}{5}$, 2.4
9. $\frac{3}{4}$, 0.75   **12.** $\frac{35}{12}$, 2.917

EXERCISE 18b
1. 1.8807   **4.** 0.3019   **7.** 4.8716   **10.** 1.1184
2. 0.2493   **5.** 0.0805   **8.** 1   **11.** 0.0524
3. 0.5890   **6.** 3.0777   **9.** 0.5774   **12.** 0.5635

13. 10.1°   **16.** 23.4°   **19.** 42.7°   **22.** 69.6°
14. 19.6°   **17.** 53.7°   **20.** 38.7°   **23.** 42.7°
15. 55.0°   **18.** 32.3°   **21.** 17.8°   **24.** 0.1°

EXERCISE 18c
1. 32.0°   **3.** 23.2°   **5.** 51.3°
2. 63.4°   **4.** 35.8°   **6.** 60.9°

7. 31.0°   **9.** 48.4°   **11.** 34.2°
8. 51.3°   **10.** 47.7°

EXERCISE 18d Some teachers may prefer to write $\tan 32° = \dfrac{x}{4}$.
1. 2.44 cm   **4.** 6.12 cm   **7.** 5.62 cm   **10.** 7.54 cm
2. 5.40 cm   **5.** 17.0 cm   **8.** 22.2 cm   **11.** 3.60 cm
3. 2.56 cm   **6.** 81.8 cm   **9.** 2.82 cm   **12.** 11.4 cm

13. 2.42 cm   **15.** 46.6 cm   **17.** 4.69 cm   **19.** 0.976 cm
14. 1.76 cm   **16.** 10.4 cm   **18.** 366 cm   **20.** 69.5 cm

EXERCISE 18e
1. 0.8862   **4.** 0.1564   **7.** 0.8625   **10.** 0.4664
2. 0.9397   **5.** 0.2622   **8.** 0.5   **11.** 0.2723
3. 0.2470   **6.** 0.6088   **9.** 0.9903   **12.** 0.9988

13. 15.7°   **16.** 65.4°   **19.** 37.9°
14. 26.2°   **17.** 41.8°   **20.** 46.7°
15. 31.6°   **18.** 21.8°   **21.** 7.1°

EXERCISE 18f
1. 30°
2. 17.5°
3. 48.6°
4. 44.4°
5. 14.5°
6. 62.7°
7. 44.4°
8. 41.8°
9. 23.6°
10. 19.5°
11. 4.38 cm
12. 10.6 cm

13. 1.46 cm
14. 4.57 cm
15. 11.7 cm
16. 23.2 cm
17. 6.31 cm
18. 21.9 m
19. 3.34 cm
20. 45.7 cm

EXERCISE 18g
1. 0.8480
2. 0.7455
3. 0.1392
4. 0.6717
5. 0.5
6. 0.9632
7. 0.6143
8. 0.6561
9. 0.3040

10. 69.7°
11. 20.6°
12. 44.0°
13. 69.6°
14. 51.1°
15. 71.6°
16. 30.1°
17. 89.2°
18. 85.8°

EXERCISE 18h
1. 34.9°
2. 36.9°
3. 45.6°
4. 48.2°
5. 48.2°
6. 53.1°
7. 50.2°
8. 66.4°
9. 81.4°
10. 25.8°
11. 34.0°

12. 3.50 cm
13. 26.9 m
14. 1.96 cm
15. 11.6 cm
16. 38.2 cm
17. 2.90 cm
18. 17.1 cm
19. 2.23 cm
20. 4.12 cm
21. 13.5 cm

EXERCISE 18i
1. 40.0°
2. 33.6°
3. 51.3°
4. 42.8°
5. 35.5°
6. 33.7°
7. 39.8°
8. 33.7°
9. 37.7°
10. 53.1°
11. 68.5°
12. 14.5°
13. 56.9°
14. 37.8°
15. 39.3°
16. 55.6°
17. 42.1°
18. 66.2°

19. 6.69 cm
20. 19.3 cm
21. 8.03 cm
22. 4.86 cm
23. 4.48 cm
24. 80.5 cm
25. 6.04 cm
26. 3.50 cm
27. 13.7 cm
28. 3.08 cm
29. 113 cm
30. 2.59 cm
31. 9.99 cm
32. 7.45 cm
33. 14.5 cm
34. 21.4 cm
35. 74.5 cm
36. 60.6 cm

EXERCISE 18j
1. 4.13 cm
2. 8.72 cm
3. 23.3 cm
4. 4.67 cm
5. 14.9 cm
6. 17.0 cm
7. 4.40 cm
8. 14.9 cm
9. 33.1 cm
10. 42.6 cm

EXERCISE 18k Angles of elevation and depression will need revision. There are more problems using trigonometry in Chapters 20 and 21.

1. 8.99 cm
2. 47.7 m
3. 143 m
4. 39.8°
5. 61.6°
6. 56.3°
7. 48.2°
8. 11.3°
9. b) 5.30 cm   c) 6.25 cm
10. a) 5.20 cm   b) 15.6 cm²
11. 4.66 m
12. a) $A\hat{O}B = 72°$, $O\hat{A}B = 54°$
    b) 6.88 cm
    c) 34.4 cm², 172 cm²

CHAPTER 19   Pythagoras' Theorem

All squares and square roots have been obtained from calculators. Tables can be used but the pupils will need reminding of how to use them and this is explained in Book 2.

EXERCISE 19a

1. 38.44	**5.** 0.5041	**9.** 9.7344	**13.** 27 140 000
2. 187.69	**6.** 0.003 481	**10.** 0.000 973 44	**14.** 2714
3. 58 564	**7.** 0.000 002 89	**11.** 84.64	**15.** 0.2714
4. 7 728 400	**8.** 97 344	**12.** 8464	**16.** 0.002 714

17. 3.142	**21.** 0.2195	**25.** 1.619	**29.** 0.6790
18. 4.461	**22.** 0.069 43	**26.** 0.2490	**30.** 2.147
19. 11.14	**23.** 9.798	**27.** 0.027 93	**31.** 21.47
20. 311.1	**24.** 17.92	**28.** 0.7071	**32.** 0.021 47

EXERCISE 19b

1. 10.3 m	**4.** 136 cm	**7.** 12.6 cm	**10.** 5.31 cm
2. 15.3 m	**5.** 23.0 cm	**8.** 7.97 cm	**11.** 0.8 cm
3. 3.22 m	**6.** 102 cm	**9.** 2.31 cm	**12.** 73.3 cm

13. 50 cm	**16.** 100 cm
14. 26 cm	**17.** 2.4 cm
15. 4.4 cm	**18.** 20 cm

EXERCISE 19c This revises work done in Book 2. Remind pupils again to use at least four significant figures if possible, when writing down the intermediate steps.

1. Yes	**3.** No	**5.** Yes
2. Yes	**4.** No	**6.** No

Some pupils may be interested in the following variation of Pythagoras' Theorem.

If any mathematically similar figures are drawn on the three sides of a right-angled triangle, a result similar to Pythagoras' Theorem applies, e.g.

a) if three equilateral triangles are drawn on the sides as shown then

area A = area B + area C

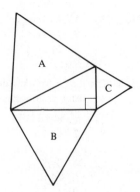

b) if three semicircles
   are drawn on the sides then

   area 1 = area 2 + area 3

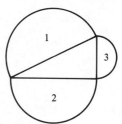

EXERCISE 19d **1.** 18.9 cm   **5.** 20.5 cm   **9.** 3.58 cm   **12.** 3.13 cm
                  2. 6.52 cm   **6.** 4.16 cm   **10.** 64.5 cm   **13.** 26.2 cm
                  3. 2.02 cm   **7.** 0.05 cm   **11.** Yes   **14.** Yes, $\hat{\text{M}} = 90°$
                  4. 0.0265 cm   **8.** 13.0 cm

EXERCISE 19e **1.** 8.94 units   **3.** 5.52 m, 35.4°   **5.** 21.2 cm
                  2. 38.8 n.m.   **4.** 0.589 cm

                  6. a) 39.4 cm   b) 47.9°
                  7. a) 2.4 cm   b) 4.64 cm   No. $AC^2 \neq AB^2 + BC^2$
                  8. c) AC = 7.07 cm, AD = 8.66 cm, AE = 10 cm
                  9. Use 7 cm and 4 cm or 8 cm and 1 cm. $\sqrt{65} = 8.06$

EXERCISE 19f Many pupils do not find it easy to draw three dimensional figures on paper or to extract other figures from them. A lot of practice in drawing cuboids and then triangles from the cuboid is recommended.

   1. a) EA = FB = GC = HD; AB = EF = HG = DC; BC = FG = EH = AD;
              24 right angles
         b) EB = 5 cm, $\hat{\text{EBA}}$ = 36.9°   c) FC = 12.4 cm, $\hat{\text{FCB}}$ = 14.0°
   2. a) AC = 12.6 cm   b) $\hat{\text{EAC}}$ = 90°, EC = 13 cm, $\hat{\text{ECA}}$ = 13.3°
   3. a) FC = 8.25 cm   b) AF = 5.39 cm, $\hat{\text{FAB}}$ = 21.8°
         c) EG = 9.43 cm, 32.0°

EXERCISE 19g **1.** a) 14.4 cm   b) 15.3 cm   c) 19.1°
                  2. a) 3.61 cm   b) 33.7°   c) 6.71 cm
                  3. a) 10 cm   b) 15.6 cm   c) 39.8°
                  4. a) 14.9 cm   b) 19.1 cm   c) 19.1 cm   d) 47.5°   e) 47.7°
                  5. 24.7 cm
                  6. a) 15 cm   b) 16.6 cm   c) 25.0°
                  7. a) 7.07 cm   b) 7.07 cm   c) 600 cm²
                  8. a) 33.7°   b) 56.3°   c) 31.4°
                  9. a) 7.07 cm   b) 336 cm²

EXERCISE 19h **1.** a) AB = DC = FE, BC = AD, EC = FD, 14 right angles
                     b) $\hat{\text{EBC}}$ = 33.7°, BE = 7.21 cm
                     c) AC = 11.7 cm, $\hat{\text{CAB}}$ = 31.0°, Yes
                     d) AE = 12.3 cm, AE = FB

2. a) 3.00 cm   b) 7.42 cm   c) 10.9 cm   d) 15.4°
3. a) 27.5 m   b) 48.5 m   c) 29.2 m   d) 49.5 m
   e) 11.6 m   f) 53.8°
4. a) 24.4°   b) 13.9°
5. a) 2.62 cm   b) 3.98 cm   c) 5.76 cm

EXERCISE 19i   **1.** a) $A\hat{B}C$, $B\hat{C}D$, $C\hat{D}A$, $D\hat{A}B$, $A\hat{F}B$, $B\hat{F}C$, $C\hat{F}D$, $D\hat{F}A$, $B\hat{F}E$, $C\hat{F}E$, $D\hat{F}E$, $A\hat{F}E$.
(12). AE = BE = CE = DE
   b) AC = 2.83 cm, AF = 1.41 cm
   c) EF = 5.83 cm, $E\hat{C}F$ = 76.4°
2. a) AC = 5.66 cm, AF = 2.83 cm
   b) AE = 5.74 cm, $E\hat{A}F$ = 60.5°
   c) EG = 5.39 cm, $E\hat{G}F$ = 68.2°
3. a) $E\hat{B}A$ = 36.9°, $E\hat{D}A$ = 45°
   b) 5 cm   c) 5.83 cm
4. a) PR = 8.54 cm   b) PY = 4.27 cm
   c) 54.5°   d) 7.37 cm

EXERCISE 19j   **1.** a) 7.28 m   b) 31.2°   c) 23.3 m, 17.3°
2. a) AC = CD′ = AD′ = 5.66 cm. Equilateral triangle
   b) Rectangle; AC′ = A′C = BD′ = DB′ = 6.93 cm
3. a) BD = 8.49 m, BE = 4.24 m
   b) EF = 4.24 m. Height = 8.49 m
   c) 45°
4. a) 7.07 cm   c) 4.85 cm
5. a) BD = 8.94 cm   b) $D\hat{B}A$ = 26.6°
   c) 11.3 cm
   d) DC = BD = 8.94 cm   e) $D\hat{C}A$ = $D\hat{B}A$ = 26.6°

CHAPTER 20   Three Figure Bearings

This chapter gives an opportunity to practice angle calculations and the use of Pythagoras' Theorem and Trigonometry.

EXERCISE 20a Revises three figure bearings.

1.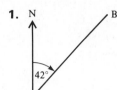

2.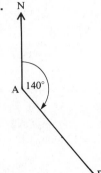

3.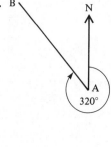

4.

6.

8.

5.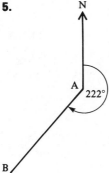

7.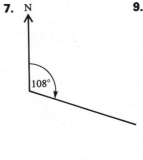

9.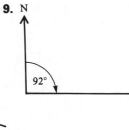

10. 062°   **12.** 328°   **14.** 249°   **16.** 154°
11. 098°   **13.** 262°   **15.** 254°   **17.** 050°

18.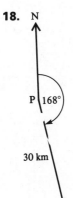

19.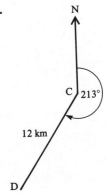

20.

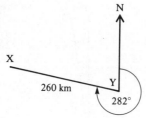

21.

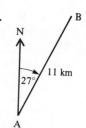

22.

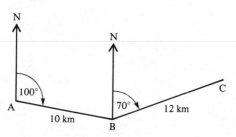

23.

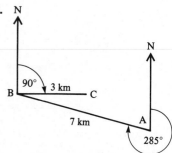

24.

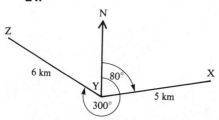

25.

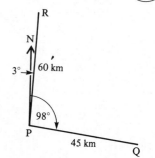

26.

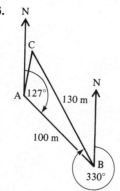

27.

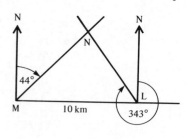

EXERCISE 20b　**1.** 240°　**3.** 342°　**5.** 172°
　　　　　　　　　2. 112°　**4.** 032°　**6.** 305°

EXERCISE 20c

1.

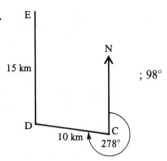

; 98°

5.

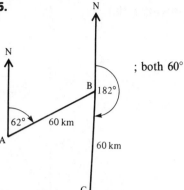

; both 60°

2.

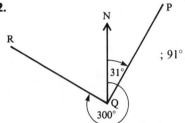

; 91°

6.

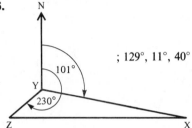

; 129°, 11°, 40°

3.

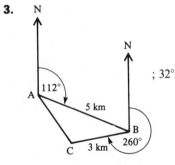

; 32°

7.

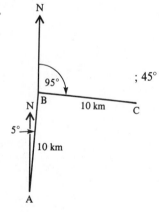

; 45°

4.

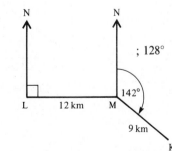

; 128°

8.

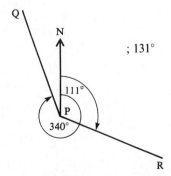

; 131°

EXERCISE 20d   1.

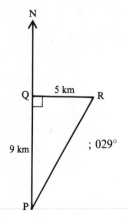

9 km   ; 029°

5.

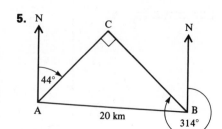

a) 46°, 44°, 90°   b) 14.4 km

2.

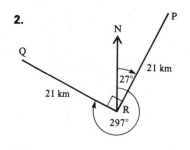

; 90°, 29.7 km

6.

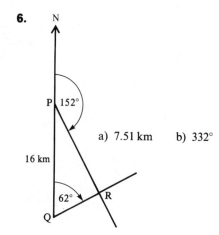

a) 7.51 km   b) 332°

3.

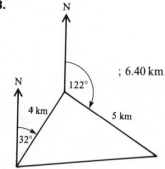

; 6.40 km

7.

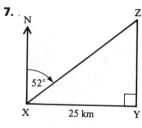

; 19.5 km, 31.7 km

4. a) 5.81 km   b) 144°

8.

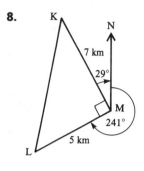

a) 54.5°   b) 186.5°   c) 007°

CHAPTER 21   Inequalities and Regions

This chapter can be used in conjunction with the chapter on straight lines because boundary lines have to be drawn or equations of lines have to be found. Squared paper is satisfactory for the graphical work and a scale of 1 cm to 1 unit is recommended. We have concentrated on shading the regions *not* required, i.e. the required region is unshaded, because this gives a neater solution which can be done on one diagram. However, because examination questions on this topic vary and sometimes they ask for the required region to be shaded, we have given some examples of this type. Exercise 21f shows how to deal with the more complicated cases when the required region has to be shaded. This is a good opportunity to emphasise the importance of reading questions carefully and giving the answer that is asked for. The last section (Exercises 21h to 21j) is a preparation for linear programming. We give an example of a linear programming problem here, which can be used with the pupils to show them the practical applications of the work in this chapter.

Linear programming problem

I need to buy at least 6 cakes and I must not spend more than 90 p. Cherry slices cost 10 p each and cup cakes cost 12 p each. Cherry slices are more popular than cup cakes so I must buy at least twice as many cherry slices as cup cakes.

I buy x cherry slices and y cup cakes. I cannot buy a negative number of cakes so $x \geqslant 0$ and $y \geqslant 0$.

I buy at least 6 cakes so $x + y \geqslant 6$:

x cherry slices cost 10 p each so their total cost is $10x$ p.

y cup cakes cost 12 p each so their total cost is $12y$ p.

I must not spend more than 90 p so $10x + 12y \leqslant 90$.

I buy at least twice as many cherry slices as cup cakes so $x \geqslant 2y$.

Draw the diagram in the usual way.

If I mark the points with integer co-ordinates we can see what choice I have about how many cakes to buy.

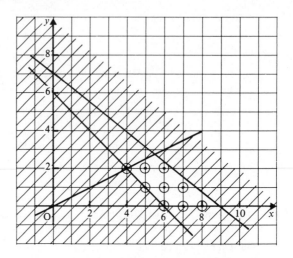

EXERCISE 21a Numbers 27 to 30 give the required region shaded.

1.
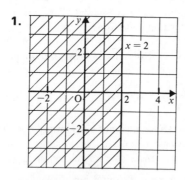

3.
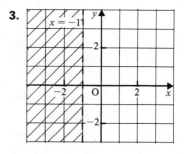

2.
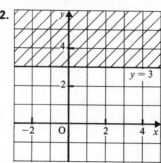

4.
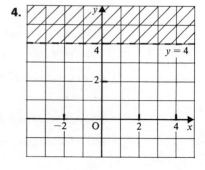

5.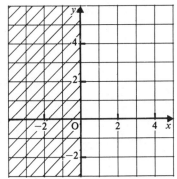

6.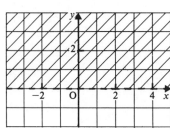

7.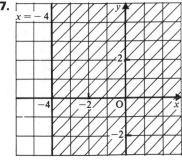

8.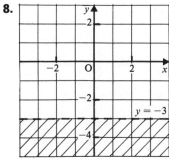

9.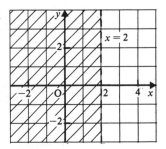

10.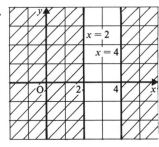

11.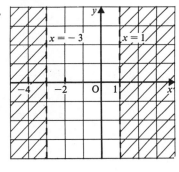

12.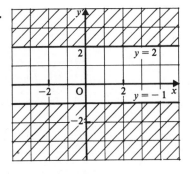

13.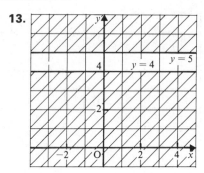

16.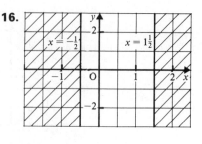

14.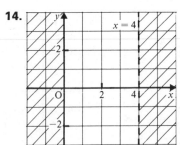

17.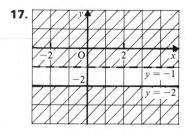

15.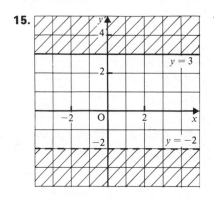

18.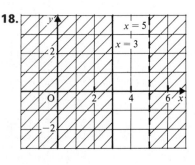

19. 10: No   11: No   12: No

20. $x \leqslant 2$

21. $y < 3$

22. $x < -1$

23. $-2 \leqslant y \leqslant 2$

24. $-1 \leqslant x < 2$

25. $-\frac{1}{2} < y < 2\frac{1}{2}$

26. 20: Yes   21: Yes   22: No   23: Yes   24: No   25: No

27. $-3 \leqslant x \leqslant 1$

28. $-4 < y < -1$

29. $2 \leqslant y < 3$

30. $3 \leqslant x \leqslant 6$

31. 27: Yes   28: No   29: Yes   32: No

EXERCISE 21b **1.**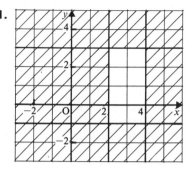

5.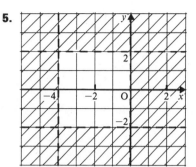

2.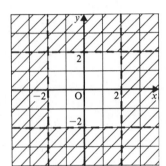

6.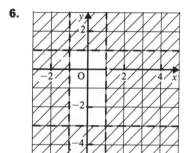

3.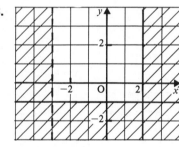

7.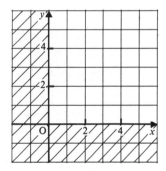

4.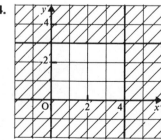

8.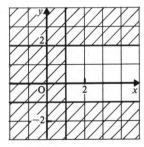

9. $-2 \leqslant x \leqslant 3, -1 \leqslant y \leqslant 2$

10. $-2 < x \leqslant 2, -2 \leqslant y \leqslant 1$

11. 9: Yes   10: Yes

12. $-2 \leqslant x \leqslant 1,\ y \geqslant -1$ **15.** $1 < x < 3,\ 1 < y < 3$
13. $x < 0,\ y > 0$ **16.** $x \geqslant -2,\ y \leqslant -1$
14. $-2 < x < 2,\ -2 < y < 2$ **17.** $x < 1,\ -2 < y < 2$

18. 16: Yes   17: No

EXERCISE 21c Some children find it easier to decide if a point is in the required region when the equation of the boundary line is in the form $ax + by = c$ so these come first in the exercise. The second section deals with boundary lines whose equations are of the form $y = ax + b$.

1.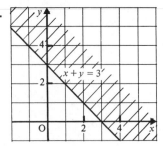

4.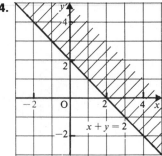

2.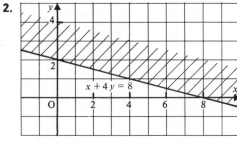

5.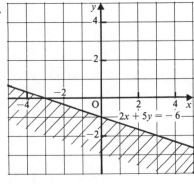

3.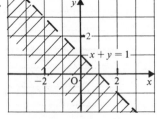

6.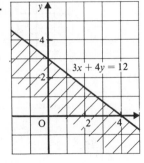

7.

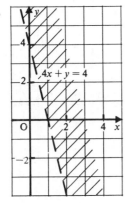

$4x + y = 4$

10.

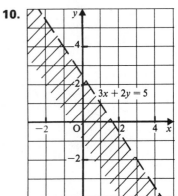

$3x + 2y = 5$

8.

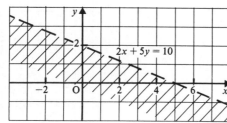

$2x + 5y = 10$

11.

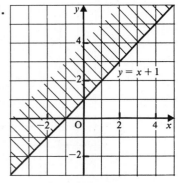

$y = x + 1$

9.

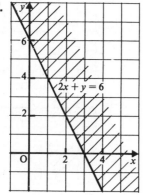

$2x + y = 6$

12.

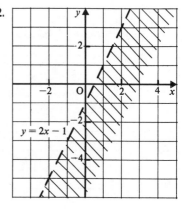

$y = 2x - 1$

13.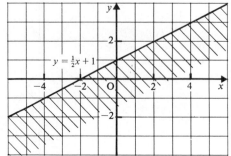

$y = \frac{1}{2}x + 1$

16.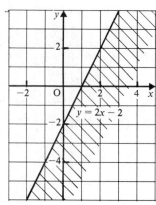

$y = 2x - 2$

14.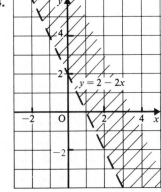

$y = 2 - 2x$

17.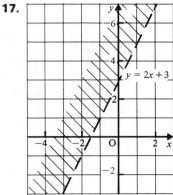

$y = 2x + 3$

15.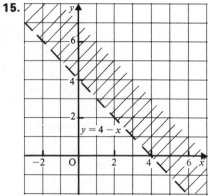

$y = 4 - x$

18.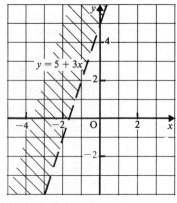

$y = 5 + 3x$

19.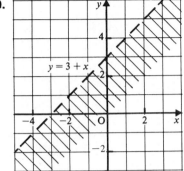

21.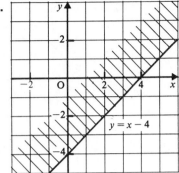

20.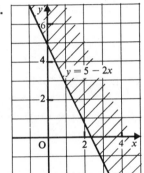

22.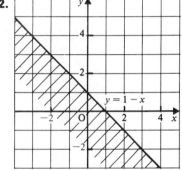

EXERCISE 21d

1. $x+y \leqslant 3$

2. $2x+y \geqslant 2$

3. $x+2y < 2$

4. $x+y < 2$

5. $3x-y \leqslant 3$

6. $2y-3x \leqslant 6$

7. $y \leqslant x+1$

8. $y > -2x-4$

9. $y \geqslant \frac{1}{2}x+2$

10. $y > -x+2$ or $x+y > 2$

11. $y \geqslant 2x-2$

12. $y < -\frac{1}{2}x+2$ or $x+2y < 4$

13. $y \leqslant 2x+2$

EXERCISE 21e Suitable ranges are $-6 \leqslant x \leqslant 6$ and $-6 \leqslant y \leqslant 6$.

1.
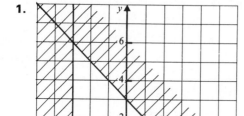

4.
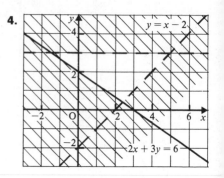

2.
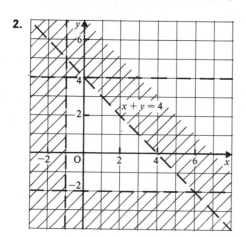

5.
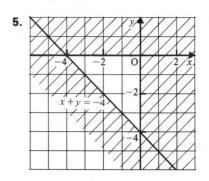

3.
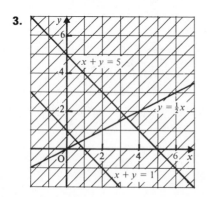

6.
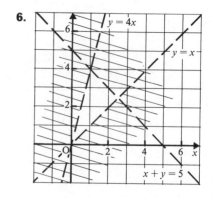

7.

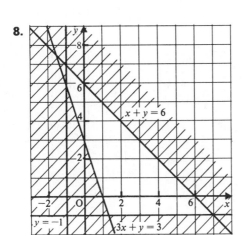

10.

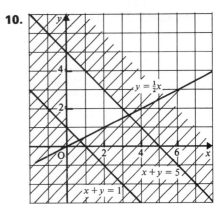

8.

11.

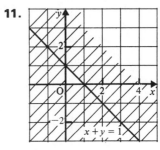

9.

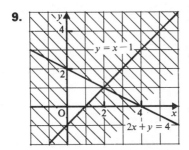

12. It does not exist
13. a) Region consists of 1 point $(1, 2)$
b) Region does not exist

EXERCISE 21f   **1.**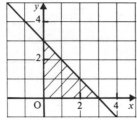

4.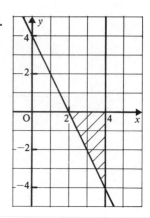

2.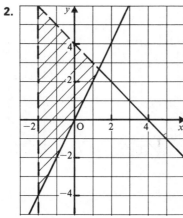

5.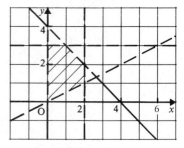

3.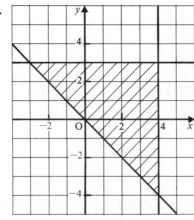

6.

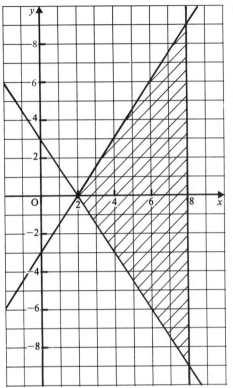

8.

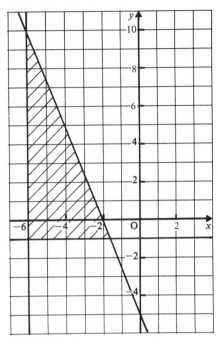

7.

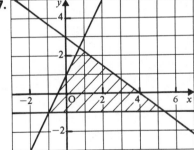

9.

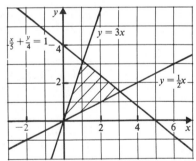

10.

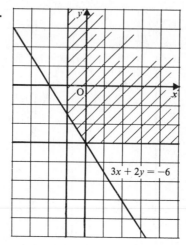

$3x + 2y = -6$

EXERCISE 21g
1. $x \geqslant -1,\ y \geqslant -2,\ x+y \leqslant 3$
2. $y \geqslant 0,\ 2y \leqslant x+2,\ x+y \leqslant 4$
3. $y \leqslant x-3,\ 2y \geqslant x-6$
4. $x \leqslant 1,\ y \leqslant x+1,\ 3x+y > -3$
5. $y > -1,\ x+y < 3,\ y \leqslant 2x+2$
6. $y \geqslant 0,\ x \geqslant -1,\ y \leqslant x+2$
7. $y < 3x+3,\ y > 3x-3$
8. $y \leqslant \frac{1}{3}x+1,\ y \geqslant -\frac{1}{3}x-1,\ y \geqslant \frac{5}{3}x-7$
9. a) $x+y \leqslant 3,\ 4y \geqslant x,\ y \leqslant x+3$
   b) $4y \leqslant x,\ x+y \geqslant 3$
   c) $y \leqslant x+3,\ x+y \geqslant 3,\ 4y \geqslant x$
   d) $4y \leqslant x,\ x+y \leqslant 3,\ y \leqslant x+3$
   e) $y \geqslant x+3,\ x+y \geqslant 3$
   f) $x+y \leqslant 3,\ 4y \geqslant x,\ y \geqslant x+3$
10. a) $x+y \leqslant 1,\ y \leqslant 2x+4$
    b) $y \leqslant 2,\ x+y \geqslant 1$
    c) $y \geqslant 2,\ y \leqslant 2x+4$
    d) $y \geqslant 2x+4,\ x+y \geqslant 1$
    e) $x+y \leqslant 1,\ y \geqslant 2x+4$
    f) $y \leqslant 2,\ y \leqslant 2x+4$
11. a) C   b) A   c) B

EXERCISE 21h
1. $(2, 2),\ (-2, 4),\ (-2, -2)$
2. $(2, 3),\ (-1, 0),\ (0, -2)$
3. $(1, -2),\ (1, 1.5),\ (6, -2)$
4. $(1, 1),\ (7, 3),\ (4, 6),\ (-4, 6)$

5. 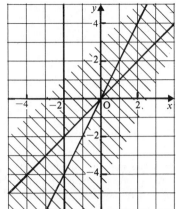 $(-2, -4)$, $(-2, -2)$, $(0, 0)$

6. 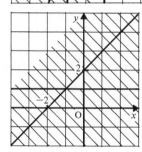 $(0, 1)$, $(0, 2)$ and $(-1, 1)$

7. 1. 19 points $(-2, -2)$, $(-2, -1)$, $(-2, 0)$, $(-2, 1)$, $(-2, 2)$, $(-2, 3)$,
$(-2, 4)$, $(-1, -1)$, $(-1, 0)$, $(-1, 1)$, $(-1, 2)$, $(-1, 3)$, $(0, 0)$,
$(0, 1)$, $(0, 2)$, $(0, 3)$, $(1, 1)$, $(1, 2)$, $(2, 2)$

  2. 4 points $(0, 0)$, $(1, 1)$, $(0, -1)$, $(0, -2)$

  3. 20 points $(-6, -2)$, $(-5, -2)$, $(-4, -2)$, $(-4, -1)$, $(-3, -2)$, $(-3, -1)$,
$(-2, -2)$, $(-2, -1)$, $(-2, 0)$, $(-1, -2)$, $(-1, -1)$, $(-1, 0)$,
$(0, -2)$, $(0, -1)$, $(0, 0)$, $(0, 1)$, $(1, -2)$, $(1, -1)$, $(1, 0)$, $(1, 1)$

8. 13 points $(-1, 0)$, $(-1, 1)$, $(-1, 2)$, $(-1, 3)$, $(0, -1)$, $(0, 0)$, $(0, 1)$, $(0, 2)$,
$(0, 3)$, $(1, 0)$, $(1, 1)$, $(1, 2)$, $(2, 1)$

9. 3 points $(1, 1)$, $(2, 1)$, $(1, 2)$

10. 9 points $(2, -1)$, $(2, 0)$, $(2, 1)$, $(2, 2)$, $(3, 1)$, $(4, 0)$, $(5, -1)$, $(4, -1)$, $(3, -1)$

EXERCISE 21i **1.** 5, 2, -4 **3.** 11, -14, 0

  2. 4, -3, 7 **4.** 5, 22; At $(2, -8)$

  5. 10, -1; At $(3, 8)$

  6. a) $(-2, -1)$, $(3, -1)$, $(3, 3)$, $(0, 3)$ b) $(3, 3)$ c) $(-2, -1)$
  d) 20   e) No

  7. a) $(6, 0)$, $(0, 3)$, $(-2, -3)$ b) $(6, 0)$

  8. a) $(4, 1)$, $(-2, 2)$, $(-2, 5)$ b) (i) $(4, 1)$ (ii) $(-2, 5)$
  c) $(-2, 3)$, $(-2, 4)$, $(-1, 2)$, $(-1, 3)$, $(-1, 4)$, $(0, 2)$, $(0, 3)$, $(1, 2)$, $(1, 3)$,
  $(2, 2)$; 10 points
  d) No

  9. b) $(5, -3)$, $(-2, 4)$, $(-2, -3)$ c) 33 points
  d) greatest at $(5, -3)$, least at $(-2, 4)$

EXERCISE 21j **1.** $(1, 2)$ **4.** $(0, 4), (1, 2), (2, 0), (3, -2)$
2. $(2, -2)$ **5.** $(0, 3)$
3. $(2, -1)$ **6.** $(0, 3)$; No

CHAPTER 22   Averages

Average speed frequently causes difficulty when different parts of a journey are travelled at different speeds. Home produced questions between different local places using different modes of transport should be found most helpful.

EXERCISE 22a This exercise revises the work on averages in Book 2 but with harder problems.

1. 46	**4.** 41.4	**7.** 765, 153
2. 40	**5.** a) 255 b) 51	**8.** 558
3. 20	**6.** a) 366 b) 61	**9.** 29°

10. 52 p	**13.** 8800 t
11. £5.75	**14.** a) £602.50 b) £794.40 c) £191.90
12. 80 cl	**15.** a) 130 b) 192 c) 62

16. a) 225 b) 25	**18.** 42.5 kg	**20.** 2
17. 17 y 5 m, 43 y 9 m	**19.** 70 kg	

EXERCISE 22b

1. 60 km/h	**4.** 90 km/h	**7.** 50 mph	**9.** 45 mph
2. 30 km/h	**5.** 18 km/h	**8.** 8 mph	**10.** 54 mph
3. 36 km/h	**6.** $262\frac{1}{2}$ km/h		

11. 260 km	**13.** 155 km	**15.** 3 hours	**17.** 20 min
12. 80 miles	**14.** 81 miles	**16.** 5 hours	**18.** 45 min

EXERCISE 22c

1. $22\frac{1}{2}$ mph	**3.** 140 km/h	**5.** 90 km/h	**7.** 40 mph
2. 50 mph	**4.** $4\frac{1}{2}$ mph	**6.** $137\frac{1}{2}$ km/h	**8.** (c)

CHAPTER 23

The work in this chapter provides a lot of extra practice in factorising quadratic expressions. It does not include those fractions which, after addition, can be further simplified by factorising the numerator and cancelling common factors. These will be covered in Book 4A.

EXERCISE 23a

1. $\dfrac{x}{4}$

2. $\dfrac{a}{2}$

3. $\dfrac{p}{q}$

4. $\dfrac{a}{b}$

5. $\dfrac{x}{y}$

6. $\dfrac{1}{2a}$

7. $\dfrac{a}{2c}$

8. $\dfrac{2}{q}$

9. $\dfrac{pq}{2}$

10. $\dfrac{a}{c}$

11. $\dfrac{a}{2}$

12. $\dfrac{z}{2}$

13. $\dfrac{b}{d}$

14. $\dfrac{1}{3x}$

15. $\dfrac{q}{2}$

16. $\dfrac{2}{3y}$

17. $\dfrac{m}{k}$

18. $\dfrac{s}{4t}$

EXERCISE 23b

1. $\dfrac{1}{x}$

2. $\dfrac{t}{s-t}$

3. not possible

4. not possible

5. $\dfrac{x}{2(x-y)}$

6. $\dfrac{(a+b)}{2ab}$

7. $p-q$

8. $\dfrac{1}{(4-a)}$

9. not possible

10. $\dfrac{1}{v}$

11. $\dfrac{y}{x+y}$

12. $\frac{1}{2}$

13. $\dfrac{2a}{3(a-b)}$

14. $\dfrac{2(x-y)}{3xy}$

15. not possible

16. $u-v$

17. not possible

18. $\dfrac{1}{(s-6)}$

EXERCISE 23c

1. $\dfrac{2a}{4a-b}$

2. $\dfrac{2q}{p-q}$

3. $\dfrac{1}{a}$

4. $\dfrac{3}{5}$

5. $\dfrac{2-x}{3y}$

6. $\dfrac{a}{3-b}$

7. $\dfrac{1}{3a}$

8. s

9. $\dfrac{3}{a}$

10. $\dfrac{2x}{3x-y}$

11. $\dfrac{3a}{a+b}$

12. $\dfrac{p+q}{5}$

13. $\dfrac{1}{3}$

14. $\dfrac{3+a}{4b}$

15. $\dfrac{2-y}{x}$

16. $\dfrac{1}{3y}$

17. a

18. $\dfrac{p}{2}$

19. $\dfrac{1}{a-2}$

20. $\dfrac{1}{x-4}$

21. $\dfrac{1}{y+2}$

22. $\dfrac{2}{a+3}$

23. $\dfrac{3}{x+3}$

24. $\dfrac{9}{y+2}$

25. $\dfrac{y}{x-2}$

26. $\dfrac{q}{p+2}$

27. $\dfrac{t}{s-7}$

28. $\dfrac{1}{p+3}$ **30.** $\dfrac{2}{x-4}$ **32.** $\dfrac{v}{u+6}$

29. $\dfrac{1}{x+6}$ **31.** $\dfrac{3}{x-4}$ **33.** $\dfrac{y}{x-2}$

EXERCISE 23d   1. $\dfrac{x+3}{2x-1}$ **7.** $\dfrac{x-y}{3x-2y}$

2. $\dfrac{4}{x+2}$ **8.** $\dfrac{2-x}{y}$

3. $\dfrac{2x-1}{x-2}$ **9.** $-a$

4. $\dfrac{1}{2-x}$ **10.** $\dfrac{y+3}{2y+1}$

5. $\dfrac{a+b}{a-b}$ **11.** $\dfrac{x-3y}{x}$

6. $\dfrac{a+b}{2a+b}$ **12.** $\dfrac{4x+1}{4x}$

13. $\dfrac{2x-3}{x-5}$ **17.** $\dfrac{2(2x-1)}{x-3}$

14. $\dfrac{-1}{1+a}$ **18.** $\dfrac{x-2y}{y}$

15. $a+b$ **19.** $\dfrac{1-x}{3(x+2)}$

16. $\dfrac{-(x+5)}{(x+1)}$ **20.** $\dfrac{1+y}{x+y}$

EXERCISE 23e   1. $\dfrac{ac}{bd}$ **3.** $\dfrac{5(x-y)}{2x}$ **5.** $\dfrac{a}{bc}$ **7.** $\dfrac{3(a-b)}{4(a+b)}$

2. $\dfrac{ad}{bc}$ **4.** $\dfrac{x(x-y)}{10}$ **6.** $\dfrac{ac}{b}$ **8.** $\dfrac{(x-2)(x+3)}{3}$

9. $\dfrac{x-2}{3(x+3)}$ **14.** $\dfrac{2b^2}{5}$ **19.** $\dfrac{a}{4b}$ **24.** 6

10. $\dfrac{pr}{q}$ **15.** $\dfrac{pq}{6}$ **20.** $\dfrac{a^3}{b^3}$ **25.** $x-3$

11. $\dfrac{6b}{a}$ **16.** $\dfrac{x}{2y}$ **21.** $\dfrac{1}{4(b-2)}$ **26.** $x-3$

12. $\dfrac{q}{2p}$ **17.** $\dfrac{1}{2b}$ **22.** $2(x-2)$ **27.** $\dfrac{1}{x-2}$

13. $\dfrac{12y}{x}$ **18.** $\dfrac{2}{3p}$ **23.** $2(a+3)$ **28.** $\dfrac{2}{x+4}$

29. $\dfrac{3(x-2)}{5(x+6)}$ **31.** $\dfrac{3}{3x+2}$ **33.** $\dfrac{2x-1}{6x+1}$ **35.** $\dfrac{-c(a+b)}{b}$

30. $\dfrac{2(2x-3)}{9}$ **32.** $\dfrac{2x-3}{2}$ **34.** a **36.** $(x-4)(x-2)$

EXERCISE 23f A reminder, with explanation, is needed yet again that, for example, a cannot be cancelled in $\dfrac{3}{ab} + \dfrac{a}{2}$. Numerical examples show this clearly,

e.g. $\dfrac{1}{2} + \dfrac{4}{5}$ is *not* $1\dfrac{2}{5}$ $\left(\dfrac{1}{\cancel{2}_1} + \dfrac{\cancel{4}^2}{5} = 1\dfrac{2}{5} \right)$.

1. pq	**6.** ad	**10.** xy	**15.** st
2. rst	**7.** uvw	**11.** $2x^2$	**16.** $3p^2$
3. 30	**8.** 168	**12.** $3pq$	**17.** $5ab$
4. abc	**9.** pqr	**13.** $2x^2y$	**18.** $3pq^2$
5. $wxyz$		**14.** abc	

19. $6x$	**21.** $18a$	**23.** a^2b	**25.** $12x$
20. $8x$	**22.** 60	**24.** $30x$	**26.** $15y$
			27. $12x$

EXERCISE 23g

1. $\dfrac{x+y}{xy}$	**7.** $\dfrac{2y-3x}{xy}$	**13.** $\dfrac{5}{4y}$
2. $\dfrac{3q+2p}{pq}$	**8.** $\dfrac{4q+6p}{3pq}$	**14.** $\dfrac{1}{8p}$
3. $\dfrac{2t-s}{st}$	**9.** $\dfrac{3y-2x}{xy}$	**15.** $\dfrac{13}{8a}$
4. $\dfrac{6b+a}{2ab}$	**10.** $\dfrac{20b+21a}{28ab}$	**16.** $\dfrac{4}{21x}$
5. $\dfrac{5y-6x}{15xy}$	**11.** $\dfrac{5}{6x}$	**17.** $\dfrac{6}{35x}$
6. $\dfrac{2b+5a}{2ab}$	**12.** $-\dfrac{1}{35x}$	**18.** $\dfrac{1}{3y}$

19. $\dfrac{3a+2b}{4ab}$	**25.** $\dfrac{2s+ts^2}{2t^2}$	**31.** $\dfrac{10y-3}{14xy}$
20. $\dfrac{ab-2a^2}{2b^2}$	**26.** $\dfrac{15b+4}{6ab}$	**32.** $\dfrac{18b-3a}{2a^2b}$
21. $\dfrac{3y-4}{xy}$	**27.** $\dfrac{3+2x}{3x^2}$	**33.** $\dfrac{3x^2-3y^2}{2xy}$
22. $\dfrac{4-3p}{2p^2}$	**28.** $\dfrac{4y^2-9x^2}{6xy}$	**34.** $\dfrac{14q-15p}{18pq}$
23. $\dfrac{9a^2+2b^2}{12ab}$	**29.** $\dfrac{5y+4x}{8xy}$	**35.** $\dfrac{5a^2+4ab}{5b^2}$
24. $\dfrac{10q-3p}{4pq}$	**30.** $\dfrac{pq+3p^2}{3q^2}$	**36.** $\dfrac{21+8p}{15pq}$

EXERCISE 23h

1. $\dfrac{9x+3}{20}$	**5.** $\dfrac{1-2x}{35}$	**9.** $\dfrac{5-22x}{21}$	**14.** $\dfrac{22-7x}{20}$
2. $\dfrac{5-x}{12}$	**6.** $\dfrac{7x+3}{10}$	**10.** $\dfrac{7x+9}{12}$	**15.** $\dfrac{10-5x}{6}$
3. $\dfrac{13x+1}{15}$	**7.** $\dfrac{3x+9}{35}$	**11.** $\dfrac{22-13x}{6}$	**16.** $\dfrac{31x-6}{24}$
4. $\dfrac{4x+13}{12}$	**8.** $\dfrac{5x-3}{42}$	**12.** $\dfrac{11-7x}{12}$	**17.** $\dfrac{11-7x}{10}$
		13. $\dfrac{20-17x}{24}$	**18.** $\dfrac{2-11x}{18}$

19. $\dfrac{26x+34}{15}$ **23.** $\dfrac{27x+3}{14}$ **27.** $\dfrac{3a+6}{a(a+3)}$ **31.** $\dfrac{5a+12}{a(a+4)}$

20. $\dfrac{17x-1}{12}$ **24.** $\dfrac{19x-73}{9}$ **28.** $\dfrac{6x+4}{x(x+2)}$ **32.** $\dfrac{7x-4}{x(x-1)}$

21. $\dfrac{5x-19}{21}$ **25.** $\dfrac{26x-18}{15}$ **29.** $\dfrac{7x-4}{2x(x-4)}$ **33.** $\dfrac{11x+1}{3x(2x+1)}$

22. $\dfrac{42x-49}{10}$ **26.** $\dfrac{-17x+104}{30}$ **30.** $\dfrac{2x-3}{4x(2x+1)}$ **34.** $\dfrac{21x-6}{5x(2x+3)}$

EXERCISE 23i   **1.** $\dfrac{2c-ab}{ac}$ **6.** $\dfrac{1}{x+2}$ **11.** $\dfrac{8}{15}$ **16.** $\dfrac{25}{12x}$

2. $\dfrac{qr^2}{p}$ **7.** $\dfrac{-p}{p+q}$ **12.** $\dfrac{23}{20x}$ **17.** $\dfrac{25}{24x^2}$

3. $\dfrac{7x-14}{12}$ **8.** $\dfrac{12-2x}{3x^2}$ **13.** $\dfrac{3}{10x^2}$ **18.** $\dfrac{3}{2}$

4. $\dfrac{a}{a-b}$ **9.** $\dfrac{1-2x}{x(x+1)}$ **14.** $\dfrac{4x+7}{10}$ **19.** $\dfrac{19x-1}{3x(x-1)}$

5. $\dfrac{1}{12x}$ **10.** $\dfrac{ab}{c}$ **15.** $\dfrac{(x+4)(2x-1)}{50}$ **20.** $\dfrac{2}{x(x-1)}$

21. $\dfrac{-a-3}{2a(a-1)}$ **23.** $\dfrac{3}{y}$

22. $\dfrac{3}{a-1}$ **24.** -1

EXERCISE 23j   Remind pupils of the difference between an equation and an expression.

1. 8   **6.** 5   **11.** 2   **17.** $-2\frac{1}{2}$

2. -5 **7.** $9\frac{3}{5}$ **12.** -18 **18.** -17

3. 6   **8.** $5\frac{1}{4}$ **13.** 3   **19.** 2

4. $1\frac{1}{3}$ **9.** -1 **14.** -1 **20.** 4

5. 10   **10.** $8\frac{3}{4}$ **15.** 21   **21.** 1

16. $\frac{4}{9}$ **22.** $-2\frac{1}{19}$

23. $-2, -1$ **26.** $-3, -3$ **29.** 1, 1   **31.** $2, -\frac{2}{3}$

24. 3, 2   **27.** $1, -4$ **30.** $\frac{2}{3}, 1$ **32.** $-2, 1$

25. $-2, -2$ **28.** $-3, -3$

33. $4\frac{1}{2}$ **36.** $-2\frac{4}{5}$ **39.** 0, 4   **41.** $\frac{1}{2}, -\frac{1}{2}$

34. $\frac{2}{5}$ **37.** -40 **40.** 3   **42.** 3

35. 2, 1   **38.** $\frac{2}{5}$

EXERCISE 23k   **1.** a) $\dfrac{b}{2}$ b) a c) $a-b$

2. a) $\dfrac{4}{3x}$ b) $\dfrac{1}{3x^2}$ c) 3

3. a) -13 b) 3, -1
4. a) $\dfrac{5x-7}{6}$ b) $1\frac{7}{10}$

EXERCISE 23I **1.** a) $\dfrac{2x}{y}$ b) $\dfrac{x-y}{2x}$ c) $x+3$

2. a) $\dfrac{1}{6p}$ b) $x-2$ c) $\dfrac{3y}{2x}$

3. a) $\frac{8}{9}$ b) 7, -2

4. a) $\dfrac{x^2-2x+12}{4x}$ b) $6\frac{1}{2}$

EXERCISE 23m **1.** a) $\dfrac{v}{uw}$ b) $\dfrac{1}{2a-b}$ c) $\dfrac{x}{3-x}$

2. a) $18s^2$ b) $2(x-2)$ c) $\dfrac{2-5x}{x(4x-1)}$

3. a) 4   b) 1, 2

4. a) $\dfrac{x}{6}$ b) 30

CHAPTER 24   The Circumcircle of a Triangle

The importance of neatness, correct use of instruments and a well sharpened pencil cannot be stressed too much at this stage.

It is probably best to let the pupil go through the construction to get the idea but then to repeat it to get the degree of accuracy required. Aim to get a figure with strong clean lines but with construction lines a little fainter.

EXERCISE 24a **2.** 5.83 cm
3. a) 10.9 cm   b) 6.3 cm
4. O is the midpoint of AB
A$\hat{C}$B $= 90°$ since it is in a semi-circle
5. a) They all pass through one point
b) It is outside the triangle
6. Yes. It passes through D
Because the trapezium is symmetrical about the perpendicular bisector of AB
No

CHAPTER 25   Household Bills

It will be most instructive if pupils can see an actual bill of the type being considered. Some may like to bring an old bill from home.

Electricity bills: Discuss the reasons for a standing charge.

EXERCISE 25a **1.** 223   **2.** 282   **3.** 474   **4.** 1257   **5.** 455

6. 842, 476, 353, 1136   **7.** 738, 301, 174, 806

8. 29 041, 29 387, 302, 30 704
9. 34 802, 35 161, 826, 36 930

10. £57.80   **12.** £98.22   **14.** £119.82
11. £264.87   **13.** £83.58   **15.** £78.09

Gas bills: The conversion from cubic feet to therms is given for information.

EXERCISE 25b **1.** 375   **2.** 209   **3.** 2115   **4.** 2868

5. 404, 184, 203, 396

6. 17 000   **9.** 320.9   **12.** £40
7. 26 400   **10.** 470.8   **13.** £170
8. 62 400   **11.** 667.7   **14.** £79

15. £371.15, 371   **17.** £483.43, 483   **19.** £101.84, 102
16. £192.38, 192   **18.** £56.49, 56   **20.** £331.18

21. £344.65   **23.** Credit by £10
22. Credit by £9   **24.** Credit by £3.40

Rates: This is a good topic to get pupils thinking about the many services that are taken for granted, but have to be paid for locally. Point out some of the pros and cons of the present system, e.g. it is easy to pinpoint who owns a property, thus making it fairly easy to collect the amount due. On the other hand it seems unfair that a single retired person must pay exactly the same as the family of four wage earners living next door in an identical house.

EXERCISE 25c **1.** £14 000   **4.** £150 000   **7.** £3 200 000
2. £76 000   **5.** £16 250   **8.** £1 564 000
3. £345 000   **6.** £73 470   **9.** £80 080 000

10. £7 242 000   **13.** 80 p   **16.** £100   **21.** £438.90
11. £592 400   **14.** 75 p   **17.** £350   **22.** £382.50
12. £3 747 000   **15.** 134 p   **18.** £720   **23.** £196
19. £295.16   **24.** £458.64
20. £564.40   **25.** £433.44

EXERCISE 25d **1.** 90 p   **4.** 94 p   **7.** £300   **10.** £820
2. 120 p   **5.** 158 p   **8.** £250   **11.** £564
3. 130 p   **6.** 163 p   **9.** £450   **12.** £356

EXERCISE 25e   **1.** £75 500
                   2. £2 088 000
                   3. £344 500
                   4. 77 p

5. £395.67
6. 84 p
7. £384

EXERCISE 25f   **1.** £215, £236.50
                   2. £390.60, £476.28
                   3. £526.40
                   4. 93 p, £273.42, £327.36

5. £652.32
6. £347.71
7. £11.10, £213.12
8. £340.56

EXERCISE 25g   **1.** £99.20
                   2. 393, £148.78

3. £110.36
4. £622.08

5. £5 372 000

CHAPTER 26   Statistics

The scales that we have used for the answers are roughly half those that the children should use.

EXERCISE 26a Revises the work on bar charts and frequency tables in Book 1.

1.

Age (yrs)	7	8	9	10	11
Frequency	7	9	11	14	9

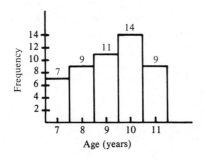

2.

Pence	0–99	100–199	200–299	300–399	400–499	500–599
Frequency	9	10	16	12	5	4

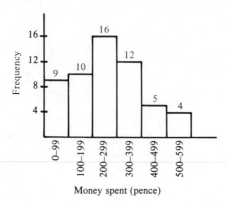

3.

Weight (g)	60–64	65–69	70–74	75–79	80–84	85–89	(suggested groups)
Frequency	3	13	6	3	3	2	

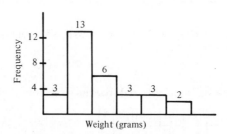

EXERCISE 26b We have avoided examples where discussion of class boundaries is necessary. With the most able, some discussion on placing continuous variables in classes with carefully defined boundaries may be desirable.

1.

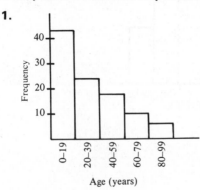

2.

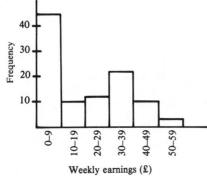

Weekly earnings (£)

3.

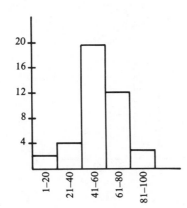

Average mark

4. Time taken (minutes)	1–10	11–20	21–30	31–40	41–50	51–60
Frequency	8	16	13	9	2	2

5. No. of hours spent watching T.V.	up to 1	1 up to 2	2 up to 3	3 up to 4	4 up to 5
Frequency	2	12	8	6	2

EXERCISE 26c   1.

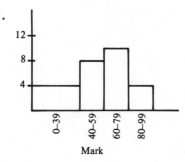

Mark

2.

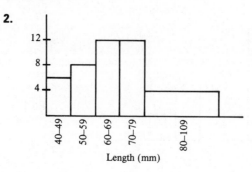

Length (mm)

3.

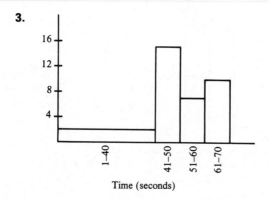

Time (seconds)

4.

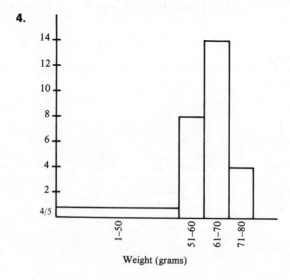

Weight (grams)

5.

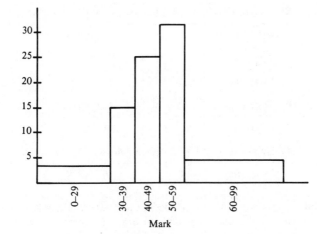

Mark

6.

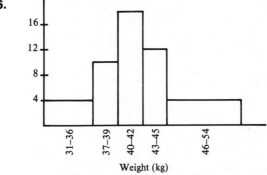

Weight (kg)

7.

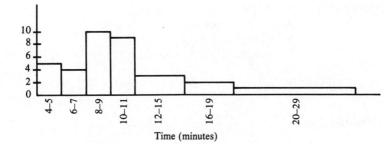

Time (minutes)

8.

Weight (kg)	1–10	11–20	21–30	31–50
Frequency	5	10	15	8

9.

Age (yrs)	1–3	4	5
Frequency	15	15	18

10.

Time (mins)	1–5	6–15	16–20	21–25
Frequency	10	18	11	6

11.

Height (cm)	10–29	30–39	40–49	50–69
Frequency	14	11	16	8

EXERCISE 26d Revises work on mean, median and mode in Book 2. Some problems ask for reasons for choosing one or other of these measures and pupils find this surprisingly difficult. As part of their general education, it is worth spending a lot of time discussing the interpretation of statistical measures.

The formula for the median, i.e. the $\frac{n+1}{2}$th value, can be deduced from a few examples.

EXERCISE 26d

	Mean	*Mode*	*Median*
1.	4.43	2	4
2.	9.67	10	9
3.	14.1	12, 13, 14	13.5
4.	1.84	1.6	1.65
5.	3.75	4	4
6.	8.42	7	8
7.	0.725	0.8	0.75
8.	1.54	1.3, 1.8	1.5

9. mean 119.2, median 124
10. mean £7150, mode £5000, median £5000
11. mean 180 p, mode 200 p, median 175 p
12. mean £21.23, median £18.10

EXERCISE 26e **1.** Modal group: 6–10 minutes
2. Mode: 1 ticket per person
3. Mode: 5 books
4. 0–19 yrs, £0–£9, 41–60 marks, 11–20 minutes, 1–2 hours

EXERCISE 26f **1.** 4.28   **2.** 3.64   **3.** 1.57   **4.** 120, 2.14

EXERCISE 26g **1.** 4.2   **2.** 7.1 cm   **3.** $50\frac{1}{2}$ p

4.

Number of defective screws per box	0–2	3–5	6–8	9–11
Frequency	10	7	2	1

, 3.1

5. 160 cm	**7.** 90.2 p	**9.** 53.5
6. 55.4	**8.** 31.9	**10.** 106.7, 106.5

CHAPTER 27   Number Bases

If this work is not required for examination purposes we would recommend that the less able do not do it, but the more able pupils will find it interesting and stimulating.

Before starting the exercises, a lot of discussion is necessary on the problems of counting and recording the results. Point out that the denary system is not the only one that evolved. There are plenty of relics of other systems, e.g. Roman numerals, duodecimal names like dozen, gross. A good visual aid is a 10×10 egg tray and a lot of ping-pong balls—this can be used for any base up to 10. Use cards to name columns and cover rows not needed. A lot of work on base 5 numbers is advisable—using handfuls, and what happens when you get to five handfuls.

EXERCISE 27a Also compare, say, 32_5 with 32_{10} and point out the difference in meaning.

1. 213_5 **2.** 2014_5 **3.** 41240_5 **4.** 30201_5

	5^3	5^2	5	unit
5.			3	1
6.			4	2
7.		4	1	0
8.		2	3	1
9.			3	4
10.			1	0
11.		2	0	4
12.		4	0	0

13. 16_{10}	**16.** 36_{10}	**19.** 17_{10}	**22.** 100_{10}
14. 14_{10}	**17.** 54_{10}	**20.** 10_{10}	**23.** 70_{10}
15. 20_{10}	**18.** 23_{10}	**21.** 4_{10}	**24.** 75_{10}

25. 13_5	**28.** 124_5	**31.** 12_5	**34.** 1003_5
26. 23_5	**29.** 133_5	**32.** 41_5	**35.** 312_5
27. 20_5	**30.** 1100_5	**33.** 110_5	**36.** 400_5

EXERCISE 27b   **1.** a)

4	1
2	3

b) 11_{10}

5. a)

8	1
5	7

b) 47_{10}

2. a)

7	1
1	5

b) 12_{10}

6. a)

5^2	5	1
2	0	4

b) 29_{10}

3. a)

4^2	4	1
1	3	1

b) 29_{10}

7. a)

3^2	3	1
2	1	0

b) 12_{10}

4. a)

2^2	2	1
1	0	1

b) 5_{10}

8. a)

9^2	9	1
5	7	4

b) 472_{10}

9. a)

	3	1
	2	1

b) 7_{10}

13. a)

4^2	4	1
3	0	3

b) 67_{10}

10. a)

	9	1
	1	8

b) 17_{10}

14. a)

2^3	2^2	2	1
1	0	0	1

b) 9_{10}

11. a)

	6	1
	2	4

b) 16_{10}

15. a)

3^3	3^2	3	1
1	2	1	1

b) 49_{10}

12. a)

8^2	8	1
1	7	5

b) 125_{10}

16. a)

6^3	6^2	6	1
1	0	0	0

b) 216_{10}

17. 21_4
18. 22_5
19. 33_7
20. 111_2

21. 23_5
22. 52_6
23. 65_8
24. 100_7

25. 22_3
26. 23_6
27. 37_9
28. 1001_3

29. 110_7
30. 108_9
31. 101101_2
32. 110100_3

33. 243_8
34. 22000_4
35. 10001110_2
36. 422_6

37. 111_6
38. 210_5
39. 1100011_2
40. 1102_7

41. 131_4
42. 15_6
43. 1111_2

44. 11100_3
45. 11302_4
46. 234_5

47. 33_8
48. 102122_3
49. 310_8

EXERCISE 27c Use whatever method the pupils are familiar with for subtraction.

1. 43_5
2. 20_3
3. 30_4
4. 11_2

5. 103_6
6. 102_3
7. 115_8
8. 1000_2

9. 122_5
10. 333_4
11. 1151_6
12. 10100_2

13. 1000_3
14. 1000_4
15. 1030_7
16. 100001_2

17. 125_6
18. 101_3
19. 3_4
20. 35_7

21. 202_3
22. 11_5
23. 226_8
24. 1_2

25. 133_4
26. 56_7
27. 33_6
28. 10_2

29. 51_6
30. 101_2
31. 646_8
32. 101_3

33. 22_5 **39.** 105_7 **45.** 414_7 **50.** 123_4
34. 12_4 **40.** 180_9 **46.** 130_4 **51.** 143_5
35. 101_3 **41.** 330_4 **47.** 242_5 **52.** 560_8
36. 120_4 **42.** 4105_6 **48.** 105_7 **53.** 2_3
37. 32_6 **43.** 1111_3 **49.** 1015_6 **54.** 214_8
38. 31_5 **44.** 1032_5

EXERCISE 27d
1. 10221_4 **5.** 2011210_3
2. 22022_5 **6.** 2116_8
3. 1110101_2 **7.** 222142_5
4. 2422_8 **8.** 220041_7

9. a) 2254_8 b) 52, 23   c) 1196_{10} d) 2254_8
10. a) 31026_9 b) 393, 52   c) 20436   d) 31026_9
11. 3047_8

EXERCISE 27e
1. a) 111_2, 101_2, 1010_2, 10000_2, 10011_2, 11000_2
     b) two
     c) 1, 10, 11, 100, 101, 110, 111, 1000, 1001, 1010, 1011, 1100, 1101, 1110, 1111, 10000, 10001, 10010, 10011, 10100
     d) when it ends in zero
     e) when it ends in one
2. 13, 11, 25, 4, 12, 29
3. a)

+	0	1
0	0	1
1	1	10

     b) 10010000_2
4. a) 6   b) 101_2
5.

×	0	1
0	0	0
1	0	1

EXERCISE 27f
1. a) 12_3 b) 22_3 c) 110_3 d) 1011_3
2. Three
3.

x	0	1	2
0	0	0	0
1	0	1	2
2	0	2	11

4. 11_3
5. a) 102_5 b) 33_5 c) 1103_5
6. $31_5 + \frac{2}{5}$ or 16.4_{10}
7. 0
8. No
9. Four, $5^3 = 1000_5$
10. Eight, $3^7 = 10000000_3$

11. a) 2, 3, 4, 5, 6, 7, 8
   b) (i) 11010_2 (ii) 1210_3 (iii) 1750_8
   c) The figures move one column to the left; i.e. the effect is the same as multiplying a denary number by ten.

12. 6   **16.** 5
13. 4   **17.** 9
14. 3   **18.** 5
15. 7   **19.** 6

20. False

EXERCISE 27g **1.** a) 6   b) 5   c) 147
                  2. a) 40_5 b) 202_3 c) 24_8
                  3. a) 341_5 b) 101_3 c) 636_8
                  4. part (c)